DATE DUE

M1630.18.C34A4   34131

CASH
SONGS OF JOHNNY

DATE DUE			
AUG 11 1970	JUL 6	'83	
MAY 11 1972	MAY 8 '92		
OCT 2 5 1972			
MAY 1 6 1973	DEC 0 3 '04		
AUG 1 4 1974			
NOV 1 3 1974			
MAR 1 9 1975			
OCT 6 '78			
MAR 3 0 '7?			
DEC 1 0 '80			
1/5/82			

D1064695

SONGS OF JOHNNY CASH

SONGS OF JOHNNY CASH

Introduction by Christopher S. Wren

Music arranged by Leo Alfassy

Designed by Ira Friedlander and Will Hopkins

The Dial Press 🦁 *New York 1970*

34131

Amsco Music Publishing Company
33 West 60th Street
New York, New York 10023
Distributor to the Music Trade

Edited by Bob Cornfield, with the assistance of Carolyn Cohn Sims. Production coordinator: Warren Wallerstein.

The editors would like to extend grateful acknowledgement to the following for their invaluable assistance and advice: Gladys Brogan, Carol Futterman, Reba Hancock, Saul Holiff, Alan Rinzler, Bob Wise, Herb Wise, Tom Levy, Dorothy Albert, Alexandra de Verney, and Gene Weintraub.

Library of Congress Catalog Card Number: 70–111446

Printed in the United States of America
First Printing, 1970

TO MY BROTHER, JACK D. CASH

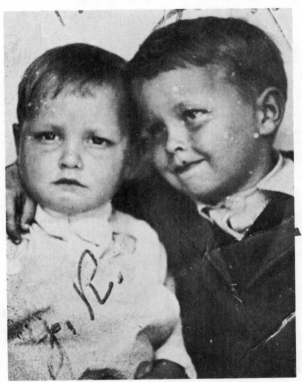

We lost you one sad day in May 1944

Though the songs that we sang

Are gone from the cotton fields

I can hear the sound of your voice

As they are sung far and wide

In loving memory

Your brother, J. R.

Table of Contents

SONGS

THE RESTLESS BALLAD OF JOHNNY CASH

Introduction by Christopher S. Wren

"It's amazing that such a nothing-looking place could mean so much to you." John R. Cash squinted across the cotton fields that defined the horizons of his boyhood in Dyess, Arkansas. It was his third trip home in ten years. A cotton stalk with a ragged boll that the picking machine had missed snapped under his soft black boot. "I can remember my mother out chopping cotton in that field when she didn't feel like it. I could pick two hundred pounds of cotton right now, not that I want to. It's something you don't forget."

As a teen-ager twenty years ago — they called him J. R. then — he picked 350 pounds a day, dragging a nine-foot-long sack down the tangled rows. Today, at thirty-eight, Johnny Cash is a superstar firmly embedded in the firmament of country music.

Such music was spawned in the rural poverty of the white South. It is Cash's world. Even in foreign fields (at the London Palladium, he broke all attendance records), Cash paces his show like a backwoods revival. Clad in black, his favorite color, he fills the stage — a towering circuit rider selling salvation. He scratches his D-28 Martin guitar high across the inlaid neck, flings it across his back, pulls two harmonicas from his swallowtailed preacher's coat. Guitar, bass, and drum behind him amplify the tempo. Converts not mesmerized in their seats walk forward in steady procession, each to pop the flashbulb of a tiny plastic camera at his sweating face.

Though he needs two corporations to handle his business — they make him possibly the only executive who cracks walnuts with his teeth — Johnny Cash can't really remember how many shows he does a year ("a couple of hundred, at least"), how many songs he's written, how many awards they've racked up. He is driven by darker recollections: when he was young, it took hours and nearly eighty pounds of cotton to fill that nine-foot sack.

Johnny Cash performs the midwifery on his uncommon songs in pencil across long yellow paper, then tucks the finished lyrics inside a black folder "to give them an air of mystery." They hit with the blunt, sometimes violent imagery of a tale told firsthand. Cash conjures up the delirium of an escaped convict dying in the desert: *Then up jumped the Devil and ran away laughing. He drank all the waterholes dry.* He crams a simple declaration with protest: *I'd sing more about more of this land, but all God's children ain't free.* Most often, the words disclose a plain-style Faulknerian preoccupation with his rural South.

Country music, if it meets any definition, tells a story. Johnny Cash, who finds hard times something to sing about, has a lot of stories to tell. In the winter of 1935, Ray Cash, a farmer busted by the Depression, put his wife, six kids, and a few belongings in an old truck. Franklin Delano Roosevelt had opened Dyess Colony, fourteen thousand scrub acres up in northeast Arkansas. A man who cleared the land would get twenty acres with a house, barn, and mule.

"I was almost four," Johnny Cash remembers, "but I remember the ice hanging off the trees. It was raining and freezing all the way up. We found house Number 266 and moved in. All us kids slept on the floor that night."

His father and oldest brother hacked out ten acres the first year and planted cotton. They killed water moccasins and a wildcat big

enough for three Cash children to lie down on the hide. A good crop brought two bales to the acre. "Dyess Colony was our salvation," says Cash. "I don't know what we would have done otherwise. Probably been following the wheat crop and going to the dogs like the others."

If FDR brought Johnny Cash to Dyess, country music pulled him away. At fourteen he was hauling two five-gallon water jugs for the work gangs along the Tyronza River. He earned two and a half dollars a day: "They kept me running as fast as I could. I'd turn on the radios in the workmen's cars when I was getting the water, and slip in and listen to the country songs."

He even answered music-magazine ads that promised to publish the songs he had begun writing. Sure he was naïve, he says. "They didn't get any of my money because I couldn't raise it. That's the only reason, though."

One July morning in 1950, Johnny Cash — still plowing with two mules — worked in the cotton fields. That afternoon, he joined the Air Force. He was trained as a radio intercept operator and sent to Germany, where he bought his first guitar. After four years, he got out as a staff sergeant.

The way he figured it, he could get into country music as a disc jockey. Heading for Memphis, he enrolled in a radio-announcing course. To support himself, he sold appliances door to door. Cash recalls that he wasn't any good: "I hated every minute. Once in a while, down in the poorest sections of town, I'd sell a used washing machine."

He also hunted the chance to sing. Three times, he asked Sun Records in Memphis for a tryout. He waited six months for one audition, arrived to find it canceled. Finally, after a year, he was given a few minutes. His songs clicked, were recorded, and sold well. A low-key ode to fidelity, "I Walk the Line," shot him into the major leagues. Cash has pulled big at record shop and box office ever since. His mileage spans twenty-six LP albums for Columbia.

A complex spirit who finds the entire world a little claustrophobic, Cash was stretched tauter by the demands of his success. About 1961, he turned to a stimulant, Dexedrine, to keep up. To relax, then, he needed a tranquilizer. He was soon locked into the cruel cycle of "nice" drugs, which were legally available on any doctor's prescription.

One night stopped him cold. "I woke up in jail in Georgia and didn't remember how I got there." A policeman had found him wandering the streets and brought him in to sleep it off. Cash quit pills then and there, outlasting the chill sweats and nightmares. "I had no trouble straightening up," he insists. "I was ready for the gutter, you know. Now I consider myself a good man. I don't make excuses. I guess this is the first time I've talked about it."

His ordeal was private, because the country-music business is still wholesome enough to worry over its own. "The guy has so much good in him," says one Nashville writer who admires Cash, "that none of his friends deserted him. John's got a miracle pulling for him, and that's June Carter."

Cash married June Carter in March 1968. "I couldn't be happy with her if I hadn't started living right," he says. June, with the kind of scrubbed good looks that college girls used to have, is full of old-fangled femininity. She rises at 5:30 A.M. to cook the family breakfast. A large Bible sits in their living room, another in the dining room. Naturally, June delivers the impromptu grace before meals. She cuts John's hair, presses his pants, serves up the squirrels that he sometimes shoots for dinner, and bakes fresh biscuits in the tiny galley of their tour bus. At the hint of criticism, she rushes to defend her man ("He's done a lot that other men would like to do if they had the guts!").

She herself is an impressive talent, bred to the country sound. An offspring of the Carter Family of folkmusic legend, June picked guitar and sang on Nashville's Grand Ole Opry for seventeen years and has sung with John in the Cash show since 1961. Their son, John Carter Cash, was born March 3, 1970.

They used to spend two-thirds of the year on the road, playing mostly one-night stands. Half the time, when the auditoriums were small, they piggybacked two shows. Now Cash's successful television show on ABC-TV keeps him at home in Tennessee for much of the year. In Nashville's Grand Ole Opry where the show is taped, in New York's Madison Square Garden, and in high school gymnasiums, Cash belts out of the right side of his mouth whatever songs come to mind onstage. June, when she isn't singing, often works with the lighting man; her guesses are the cue sheet.

Cash is most at peace when he can sprawl out in his oval living room at home or wander the woods nearby. On tour, he walls himself behind a screen of antic restlessness. The long airport waits nearly drive him crazy. He gobbles hot dogs, buys and flips through a half dozen magazines and books at a single sitting. When he loses sight of June, he yells whatever pet name comes to mind until she rushes up while onlookers stare.

June started filling a black "couth" book with suggestions for John: *Do not sing bluegrass songs in airports; do not eat sardines and crackers on airplanes.* Her hopes have not been particularly rewarded.

Small-boy mischief masks his fascination with her. "I like you better'n my first bicycle," he tells her solemnly, "or watermelon, or — hell, I dunno — a new pair of shoes on a rocky road."

A broad six feet two inches, with plow-scarred hands, Johnny Cash looks tough. He is. As a boy, he swam across the Mississippi River below Memphis. More recently, he bushwhacked his jeep up and over Tennessee's 2,126-foot Lookout Mountain in a four-hour grind. But he isn't hard. Driving home from Florida, he picked up a hitchhiker who wanted to become a singer, and gave the young man a valuable twelve-string guitar when he let him out. When the local high-school band in Hendersonville, Tennessee, was invited to the Orange Bowl, Cash put on a show and raised the travel expenses. "I'm not that damn noble," he says defensively, "but you've got to do something."

At his core, Cash has retained a Baptist spiritual conviction imparted to him by his mother, Carrie. He knows most of the Gospel stories by heart. A couple of years ago, he took his wife June to Israel, where they put together an album full of his songs and narratives about the Holy Land.

Cash has ridden causes that are intensely personal. Part Cherokee himself, he has long battled for the neglected American Indian. His bitter protest songs have become a famil-iar part of the Cash repertoire. When he can, he puts on benefits at the reservations to raise money.

Another compassion, for convicts, haunts his songs. He has played many of the big penitentiaries, with repeats at San Quentin and Folsom. At the Texas state prison in Huntsville, he stood singing in driving rain after the wet amplifiers had shorted out. In Arkansas, he helped finance a prison chapel.

"I don't see anything good come out of a prison," he argues. "You put them in like animals and tear the souls and guts out of them, and let them out worse than they went in."

The new country sound of popular music is not new to Cash. All along, he has been country, pop and folk. Now, he ranks among the top singers in any music, but he's not overly impressed.

On a recent tour, the red-and-white Cash bus was parked outside a lunch joint in southern Virginia. Inside, Johnny Cash had just swallowed a ham and egg sandwich and a bacon and tomato, ordered and eaten a steak sandwich "like that one" at the next booth, and tried a bite of June's butterscotch pie, liked it, and finished the whole wedge. He'd buy a ten-cent chocolate bar on the way out.

At another table, some teen-agers dropped a dime into the jukebox. "Folsom Prison Blues" filled the room: *I shot a man in Reno, just to watch him die.* Cash hummed along a little with himself, got bored, and chewed up the ice in his glass. Slouched in the booth, he stared out the window. Abruptly, he turned to his wife to share with her what had become the most wondrous thing in the world: "Just look at those clouds rolling the other side of that mountain, June love."

Mr. Wren, a senior editor at *Look* Magazine, is currently working on a biography of Johnny Cash.

SONGS OF JOHNNY CASH

EARLY DAYS

In 1935, Father Ray Cash (center, holding his son, Tommy) moved his family to a Dyess, Arkansas farm. Eldest son, Roy, stands beside him with his own son, Roy, Jr. Next to Roy is sister Reba. Mother Carrie holds Roy's daughter, Jan, and by her knee is daughter Joann. Beside her, Roy's wife, Dene. At this time, young Johnny Cash (opposite page) was already working a full day in the cotton fields.

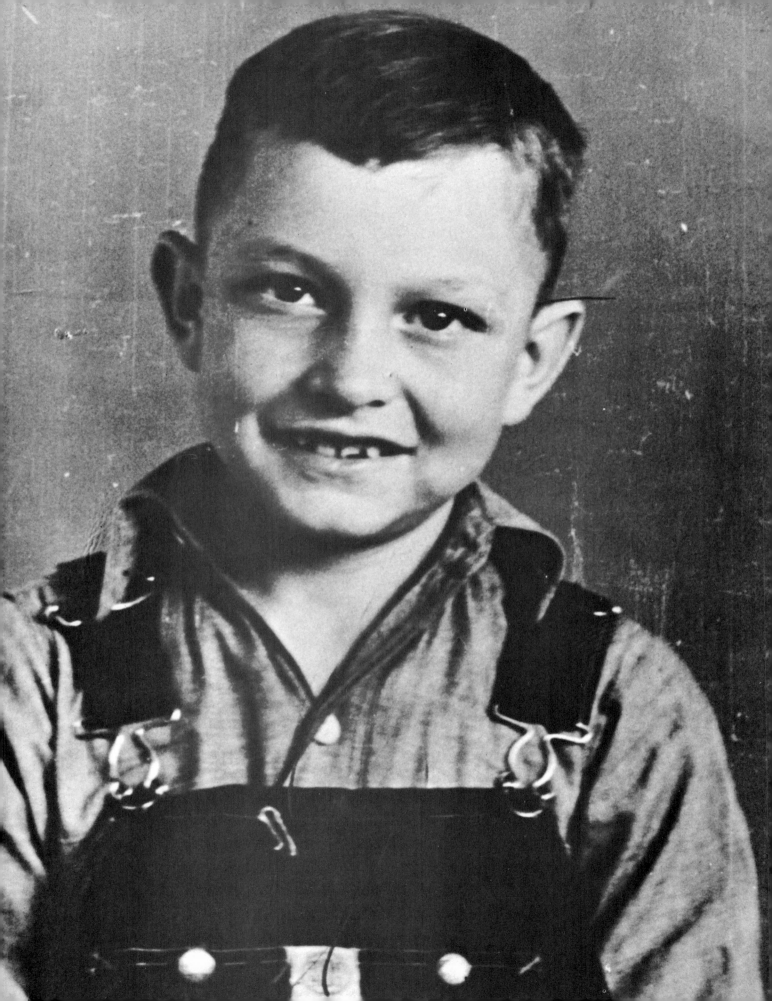

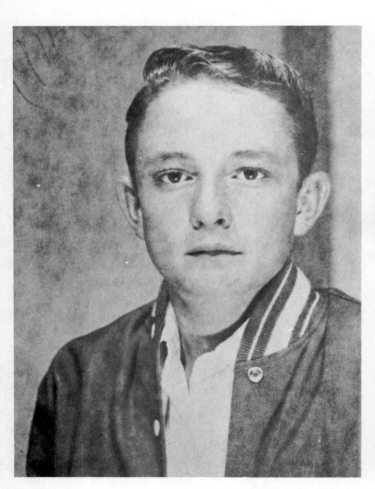

Schoolmates remember him as a quiet boy with a strong interest in swimming.

When Cash moved to California in 1959, he brought his parents with him.

Top: left to right, Mother, Father, Johnny, Tommy, Reba and Joann in Dyess. *Bottom:* Johnny Cash's first year at his house in Hendersonville was the occasion for a family reunion. Left to right, Louise, Joann, Reba, Roy, Johnny, Tommy. Papa and Mama Cash, seated.

At Dyess, Arkansas, the Cash family stands next to their first car. Johnny Cash is on the extreme right.

Cash was a Radio Intercept Operator assigned to the Air Force Security Service in Germany. His tour of duty extended from July 1950 to July 1954. Here (top row, right), with his class at Brooke Air Force Base in San Antonio.

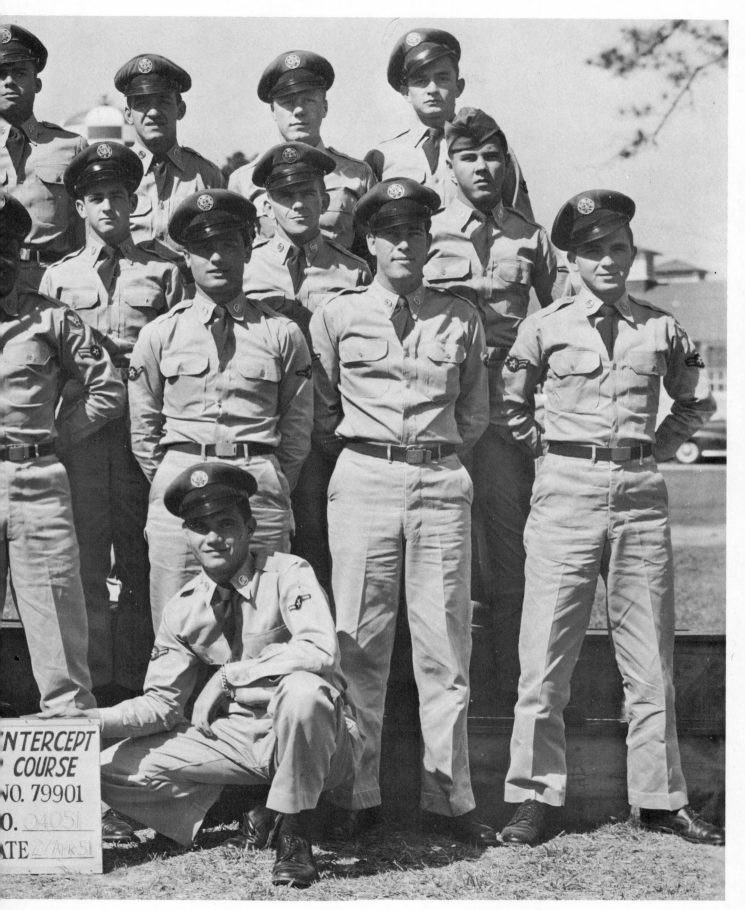

INTERCEPT
COURSE
NO. 79901
O. 04051
ATE 27 APR 51

After the Air
Force, Cash first
started singing
around Memphis.

Later, he toured
with Elvis Presley,
and with Carl
Perkins, and with
Roy Orbison. They
all began roughly
about the same
time.

He began singing from the flat beds of trucks, at church socials, at clubs, at country dances. Later, he graduated to Louisiana Hayride and the Grand Ole Opry. Cash's first great hits were: "Cry, Cry, Cry," "Hey, Porter," "Ballad of a Teenage Queen," "I Walk the Line."

Tours take Cash to Indian reservations and concert halls.

On the far left, bottom, Cash accepts a Country Music Association Award. On left, Cash is backed by Carl Perkins, Bob Wooten, and The Statler Brothers.

ON THE ROAD

Television and films have made inroads into his touring time, but Cash is still a traveling man. Here, with Carl Perkins and the troupe's luggage, at the airport in Kingsport, Tenn.

June Carter stands in the dressing room entrance at Ole Miss watching her husband perform.

The Cash Show
used to tour almost
exclusively by bus.
Here, John with
his wife, June.

June joins Johnny for a song at a one-night stand in Charleston, West Virginia, backed by The Tennessee Three (Bob Wooten, W. S. Holland, and Marshall Grant).

"No more chasin' moonbeams, or catchin' falling stars; I know now my pot of gold is anywhere you are. . . . Loneliness is emptiness, but happiness is you."

DOWN HOME

Cash returns to visit the house he had left almost twenty years before to join the Air Force. The barn is now gone, but the trees his father planted when they settled there now shadow the five-room house. "It was hard work, but it was a happy place."

John and June explore a deserted three-room "shotgun shack" down the road from his old house in Dyess.

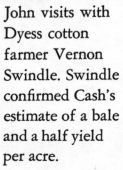

John visits with Dyess cotton farmer Vernon Swindle. Swindle confirmed Cash's estimate of a bale and a half yield per acre.

In the fields of Dyess, June Cash, an Appalachian mountain girl, learns to pick cotton from an old hand who, as a teenager, could pick 350 pounds a day.

The Original
Carter Family, with
the Singing Brake-
man, Jimmie
Rodgers, on a re-
cording session in
Louisville. Left to
right: Rodgers,
Mother Maybelle,
A. P. Carter, Sara
Carter.

The tradition of the Original Carter Family, who began singing in 1927, continues with Mother Maybelle, here backing daughter June on the autoharp with a "Carter lick." June's sister, Helen, joins in. With Anita, the three make up the present Carter Family.

Cash's 300-foot-long house in Hendersonville, Tennessee, is built into a cliff and overlooks Old Hickory Lake. A new wing has recently been added to accommodate a study for Johnny and a room for his son, John Carter Cash.

June and Johnny Cash entertain composer Shel Silverstein (with guitar), who wrote "A Boy Named Sue," in the oval living room of their home. On the right, one of John's poems is framed on the wall.

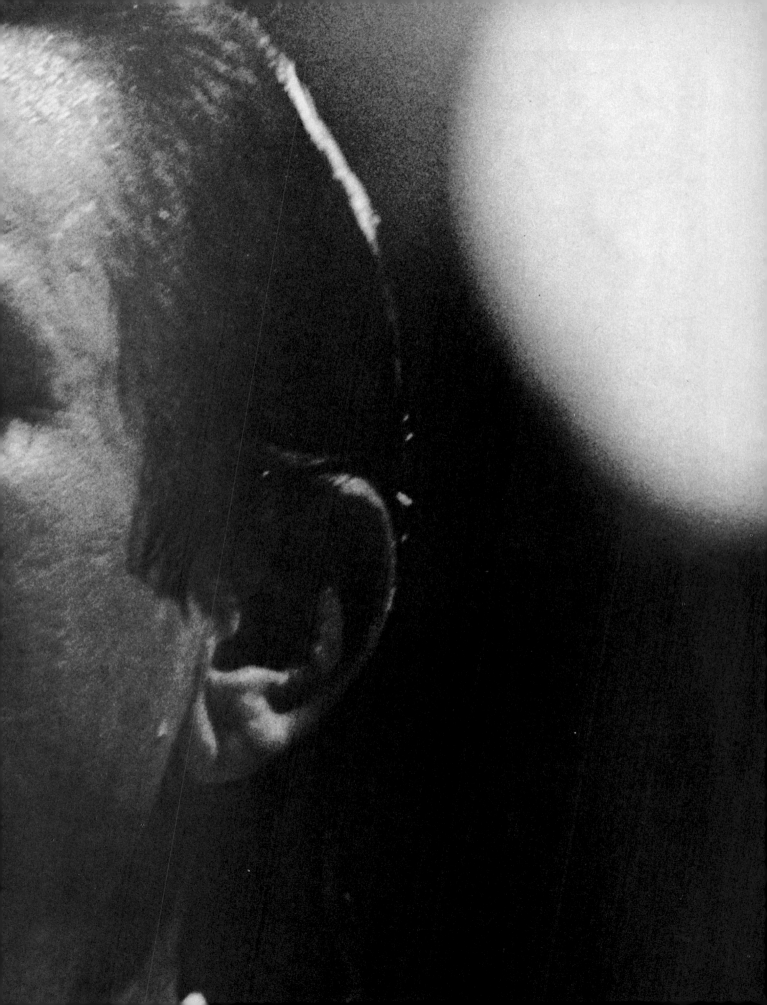

"A song is an inside thing with me," says Cash, who considers "I Walk the Line" one of his best. He writes more than half the songs he records. Cash, who cherishes his four daughters (Rosanne, Kathy, Cindy, and Tara) by a previous marriage, who live in California, here lets Rosanna, one of June's daughters, eavesdrop. She and her sister Carlene live with Johnny and June.

Cash and his
mother-in-law,
Maybelle Carter,
are not only good
music companions
but can spend
hours fishing to-
gether on Old
Hickory Lake.

John with the
Everly Brothers

Johnny Cash's
ABC-TV show is
among the top
rated in the coun-
try. It is televised
from Nashville's
Grand Ole Opry,
a hall that echoes
with the memory
of great country
performers.

Above: Bob Dylan
stands with Co-
lumbia Records
producer, Bob
Johnston, at
Nashville's Grand
Ole Opry.

Cash sings for Arkansas inmates at Cummins Prison, where he later donated a chapel for the prisoners.

"Prisoners are the greatest audience that an entertainer can perform for. We bring them a ray of sunshine in their dungeon, and they're not ashamed to respond."

"I don't see anything good come out of a prison. You put them in like animals and tear the souls and guts out of them, and let them out worse than they went in."

SONGS OF JOHNNY CASH

WHAT IS TRUTH?

Johnny Cash

2. A little boy of three sittin' on the floor
   Looks up and says: "Daddy, what is war?"
   "Son, that's when people fight and die!"
   The little boy of three says: "Daddy, why?"
   A young man seventeen in school
   Being taught the golden rule
   By the time another year's gone around
   He may have to lay his own life down.
   (sung) Can you blame the voice of youth
        for asking: "What is truth?"

3. A young man sittin' on the witness stand
   The man with the book says: "Raise your hand!"
   "Repeat after me, I solemnly swear!"
   The Judge looks down at his long hair.
   And although the young man solemnly swore
   Nobody wanted to hear any more
   And it really didn't matter if the truth was there
   It was the cut of his clothes and the length
        of his hair!
   (sung) And the lonely voice of youth cries:
        "What is truth?"

SEE RUBY FALL

Johnny Cash and Roy Orbison

SOUTHWIND

Johnny Cash

1. South - wind, _____

you picked her up in Jack - son - ville and left me cold and

78

She's gone a-gain _____ on the South-wind. _____

Repeat and fade

2. Southwind, I need a forty-dollar ticket
   and about this time tomorrow I'll be gone.
   Southwind, but if I had forty dollars
   I would buy myself a smile to carry on.
   And you go woo-oo-oo.
   She's gone again on the Southwind.

3. Southwind, take her fast and take her far
   cause that's the way she always like to go.
   Southwind, I will be waitin' for the
      roundtrip ticket
   if you'll bring her back and I done told her so.
   Don't you go woo-oo-oo.
   She's gone again on the Southwind.

SAN QUENTIN

Moderately

Johnny Cash

1. San
Quen-tin, you've been liv - in' hell to me. _____
Quen-tin, I hate ev - 'ry inch of you. _____

You've host - ed me since Nine - teen Six - ty-
You've cut me and have scarred me thru an'

three. _____
thru. _____

I've seen 'em come and
And I'll walk out a

3. San Quentin, what good do you think you do?
   Do you think I'll be diff'rent when
      you're through?
   You bent my heart and mind and you may
      my soul,
   And your stone walls turn my blood a little cold.

4. San Quentin, may you rot and burn in hell.
   May your walls fall and may I live to tell.
   May all the world forget you ever stood.
   And may all the world regret you did no good.

BEAUTIFUL WORDS

Johnny Cash

Slowly

Beau - ti - ful words, Beau - ti - ful words,

He spoke beau - ti - ful words. The

wind lay still, and the whole world lis - tened As

He spoke Beau - ti - ful words.

THIS SIDE OF THE LAW

Moderately

Johnny Cash

On this side of the law, On that side of the law, Who is right?__ Who is wrong?__ Who is weak?__ Who is strong?__ Who is for and who's a-gainst the law?__ 1. You see I 2. Well, I

did - n't real - ly | mean___ an - y | harm,_____ | But I
did - n't mean to | let my fam - 'ly | down,_____ | And I'm

sim - ply could-n't | make it on the | farm._____ | When the
not giv - ing | you the run - a - | round._____

land won't give a | lot you got-ta | do with what you | got. And
I'd much rather be dead | than have to | beg my dai - ly bread. And to

all I got's the mus - cle in my | arm; | bum! | bum! | bum! I
pay my way no mat - ter where I'm | bound; | | | Well, I

would-n't ev - er hurt my fel - low man.＿＿＿ And it
did - n't real - ly think that I did wrong.＿＿＿ So

seems to me that you could un - der stand.＿＿＿ I'm just
long as I stayed here where I be - long.＿＿＿ I did the

try-in' to help my - self with-out hurt - in' some-bod-y else. And a
on - ly thing I could, same as an - y - bod-y would. And

man has got to do the best he can.＿＿＿
I was sim-ply try-ing to get a - long.＿＿＿ On

Repeat twice
3rd time to Fine.

COME TO THE WAILING WALL

Johnny Cash

86

Thank God, you__ can__ stand up-on__ this Ho-ly Land, And touch the hal-lowed rock__ That God de-liv-ered to our Land.__

Come to the Wail-ing Wall;__ Come to the Wail-ing Wall.__

Come to the Wail-ing Wall.__

Come to the Wail-ing Wall;__ Come to the Wail-ing Wall.__

Repeat and fade

ROUTE #1, BOX 144

Moderately

Johnny Cash

1. His
dy - ing bare - ly made the morn - ing pa - per;
nev - er did great things to be re - mem - bered;

And they summed it up in twen - ty words or
He had nev - er been a - way from home be -

more: _____
fore; _____

(Spoken:)

"Killed in action.
But you'd thought he

Leaves wife and ba - by,_____ at
was president or some - thin',_____

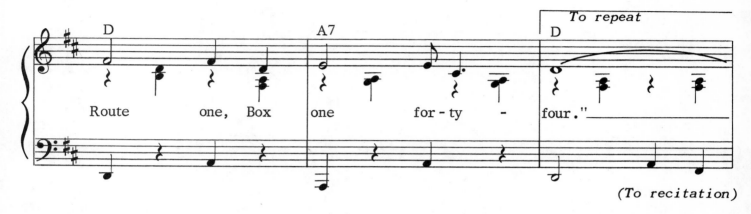

Route one, Box one for - ty - four."_____

To repeat

(To recitation)

To finish rall.

2. He four._____

(Play as many times as needed for Recitation.)

Recitation:

He grew up on a little farm
Just a couple of miles out of town.
As a boy he worked in his daddy's field.
And when his daddy could spare him
He hired out to the neighbors
For whatever they could pay him.
He was thought of as just average,
A good boy, nothing more, the average amount of friends.
He married his high school sweetheart.
They bought a little plot of ground.
A couple of miles out of town on a mailbox
It said: Route 1, Box 144.
Well, back in town, there were very few people

That really knew him because
He hardly ever came to town
Except for maybe on Saturdays and, of course,
The usual crew was always there.
But he didn't spend a lot of time with the usual crew.
He took care of his business, bought what he had to have
Or could afford for his family
And went back to his little farm.
With a baby on the way he went to the army.
And it was just a short while that the news came
That he was killed in action.
His body was sent back on a plane, and then by train
And then they brought the body from the train station
To Route 1, Box 144.

STARKVILLE CITY JAIL

Bounce tempo

Johnny Cash

1. Well, I left my mo-tel room, down at the Stark-ville Mo-tel; The town had gone to sleep and I was feel-in' fair-ly well. I strolled a-long the side-walk 'neath the sweet mag-nol-ia

threw me in the car and start-ed driv-in' in-to town; I said: "What the hell did I do?" He said: "Shut up and sit down." Well, they emp-tied out my pock-ets, took my pills and gui-tar

90

cur-few, and you go to the Stark - ville Cit - y jail."

2. Well, they

3. *I started pacin' back and forth, and now and*
   then I'd yell,
   And kick my forty-dollar shoes against the
   steel floor of my cell.
   I'd walk awhile and kick awhile, and all night
   nobody came.
   Then I sadly remembered that they didn't
   even take my name.
   At 8 A.M. they let me out. I said,
   "Gimme them things of mine!"
   They gave me a sneer and a guitar pick, and a
   yellow dandelion.
   They're bound to get you, 'cause they
   got a curfew,
   And you go to the Starkville City Jail.

'CAUSE I LOVE YOU

Moderately fast

Johnny Cash

(He): 1. I'll sweep out your chim-ney, yes, and I will bring you
2. I'll be there be - side you, if you need a cry - ing

flow - ers, yes, and I will do for you most an - y-
shoul - der; Yes, and I'll be there to lis - ten when you

thing you want me to; (She): If we live in a
need to talk to me; When you wake up in the

cot - tage, you will feel like it's a cas - tle by the
dark - ness, I will put my arms a - round you, and

roy - al way you're treat - ed and the at -
hold you till the morn - ing sun comes

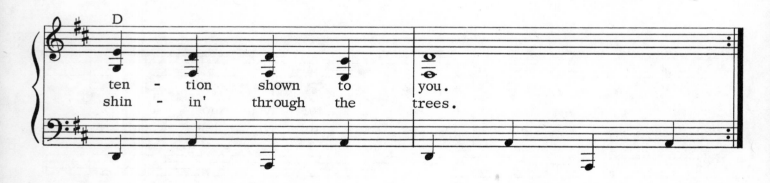

ten - tion shown to you.
shin - in' through the trees.

Chorus:

(Both):
3. I'll be right be - side you, no mat - ter where you

94

Chorus:
I will bring you honey from the bee tree in
    the meadow;
And the first time there's a rainbow, I'll bring you
    a pot of gold.
I'll take all your troubles, and I'll throw them
    in the river;
Then I'll bundle down beside you, and I'll keep
    you from the cold.
    (Repeat first chorus:)

JESUS WAS A CARPENTER

Moderately

Christopher S. Wren

1. Je - sus was a car - pen - ter, and He worked with a saw and a
found them as they wan - dered through the wild Ju - de - an

ham - mer; And His hands could form a ta - ble true e -
moun - tains; And He found them as they pulled their nets

nough to stand for - ev - er. And He might have spun His
upon the Sea of Gali - lee; And for a thou - sand

life out in the cool - ness of the morn - ings;____ But He
eve - nings, while the day be - hind Him emp - tied,____ He

put a - side His tools, And He walked the burn - ing
walked a - mong the poor, And He stopped to touch the

high - ways to build a house for folks like you and
dy - ing, and He built His house for peo - ple just and like

1. 2. 3. 4.

me. ____
these. ____

5.

2. And He

rall.

3. It was on a shining Sunday when He rode
    to old Jerusalem;
And the palms they cast before Him were the
    crimes they laid against Him.
It was on a storming Friday when he climbed
    the streets to Calvary;
And where he died today, why, they're sellin'
    beads and postcards;
And they tell us, too, that that was long ago.

4. But, would He stand today upon the sands
    of California;
Or walk the sweating blacktop in New York
    and Mississippi,
Where the mighty churches rise above the

screaming cities,
Would He be a guest on Sunday, a vagrant
    on a Monday,
With the doors locked tight against His kind,
    you know?

5. Come again, now Jesus, be a carpenter among us;
There are chapels in our discontent, cathedrals
    in our sorrows;
And we dwell in golden mansions, with the sand
    for our foundations,
And the raging water's rising, and the thunder's
    all around us.
Won't you come and build a house on rock again?
(Repeat first verse, fade out.)

LAND OF ISRAEL

Johnny Cash

might-y things that hap-pened in the Land of Is-ra-el.
nev-er more be sor-row in the Land of Is-ra-el.

Here, when Mo-ses and the Proph-ets spoke of One who would be King; Of a Heav-en-ly Mes-si-ah, and the bless-ings He will bring. Oh, to hear a-gain the call,—— All is peace-ful, all is well, Up-on ev-'ry rock and moun-tain In the Land of Is-ra-el.—— 2. From the el. rall.

HE TURNED THE WATER INTO WINE

Moderately

Johnny Cash

He turned the wa-ter in-to wine;___ (Didn't my Lord, now...)
He fed the hun-gry mul-ti-tude;___

He turned the wa-ter in-to wine.___ In the
He fed the hun-gry mul-ti-tude.___ With a

lit-tle Ca-naan town, The word went all a-round that ___
lit-tle bit of fish and bread, They said ev-'ry-one was fed.

100

YOU ARE WHAT I NEED

Moderately

Johnny Cash

1. Be-
side a sing-in' moun-tain stream where the pus-sy wil-low
leaned a-gainst the bark of birch and I breathed the hon-ey

grew, Where sil-ver leaf of maple spar-kled
dew, Saw a north-bound flock of geese a-gainst the

in the morn-ing dew. I braid-ed twigs of
sky of ba-by blue. A-mong the lil-y

3. A mockingbird sang just for me and I thanked
    him for the song,
   then darkness floated up the hill and I had
    to move along.
   Those are a few little things on which the mind
    and spirit feed
   but flesh and bloods needs flesh and blood and
    you are what I need.

THE TIMBER MAN

Moderately

Johnny Cash

1. Well, my world is green and dark and damp; My home is in the log-ging camp;
say there's saw-dust in my brain "And don't get caught out in the rain!" I

All week I cut the might-y tree; Sat - ur - day I do as I
got stump wa - ter in my blood, The sweat from the brow turns the

damn well please!___ Give the man more than his hire; And
ground to mud!___ When the men don't know how to fell a tree, The

THIS TOWN

Johnny Cash

1. This town is not for me,
2. This town wants me to go,

I won't be stay-in' 'round.
It ain't where I was bound.

This town is hard and cold;
This town don't need me here,

I'm
And

THE BALLAD OF IRA HAYES

Peter La Farge

108

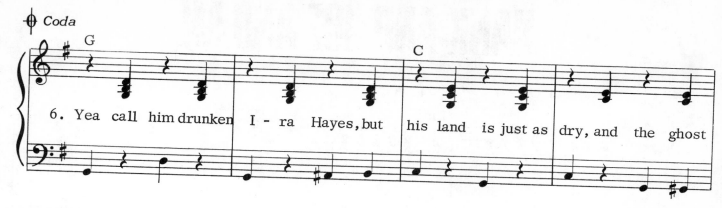

6. Yea call him drunken I-ra Hayes, but his land is just as dry, and the ghost

is lying thirsty in the ditch where Ira died.

Verses 1-5 *(Recitation)*

1. *Gather 'round me, people; there's a story
    I would tell,
    About a brave young Indian you should
      remember well;
    From the land of the Pima Indians, a proud
      and noble band;
    Who farmed the Phoenix Valley in
      Arizona Land. (D.S. 𝄋 Chorus.)*

2. *Down their ditches for a thousand years the
      waters grew Ira's people's crops.
    Till the white man stole their water rights and
      their sparklin' water stopped.
    Now Ira's folks grew hungry and their land grew
      crops and weeds.
    When war came Ira volunteered and forgot the
      white man's greed. (D.S. 𝄋 Chorus.)*

3. *Well, they battled up Iwo Jima Hill—
      two hundred and fifty men,
    But only twenty-seven lived—to walk back*

*down again;
    When the fight was over—and Old Glory raised,
    Among the men who held it high was the
      Indian—Ira Hayes (D.S. 𝄋 Chorus.)*

4. *Ira Hayes returned a hero—celebrated thru
      the land,
    He was wined and speeched and honored—
      everybody shook his hand;
    But he was just a Pima Indian—no water,
      no home, no chance;
    At home nobody cared what Ira done—and when
      do the Indians dance? (D.S. 𝄋 Chorus.)*

5. *Then Ira started drinkin' hard—jail was often
      his home;
    They let him raise the flag and lower it— as you
      would throw a dog a bone;
    He died drunk early one morning—alone in the
      land he'd fought to save;
    Two inches of water in a lonely ditch—was the
      grave for Ira Hayes. (D.S.𝄋, then to Coda ⊕.)*

109

HANK AND JOE AND ME

Johnny Cash

1. In the des-ert where we searched for gold, the days are hot, the nights are cold. Hank and Joe and me walked on, So bold and brave and free.

2. don't re-mem-ber how long I lay, but when I awoke it was the break of day. Buz-zards cir-cled miles a-head, I knew Hank and Joe were dead. My

For days and days we
eyes were dimmed, but

APACHE TEARS

Johnny Cash

Hoof prints and foot prints deep ruts the wag-ons made, the vic-tor___ and the los-er___ came by here.

No head stones, but these bones

bring mes - ca - le - ro death moans. See the smooth black

nug - gets by the thou-sands_ ly - ing here,

Pet - ri - fied_ but jus - ti - fied_ are these A-pach-e

tears._

115

Repeat and fade

THE BALLAD OF BOOT HILL

(Ad lib)

Carl Perkins

Here lies, less more, four slugs from a for-ty-four; No less, no more. Out in Ar-i-

Waltz Tempo

1. zo - na, just south of Tuc-
2. time now since the town was a

son, Where tum-ble-weeds
boom. The jail-house is

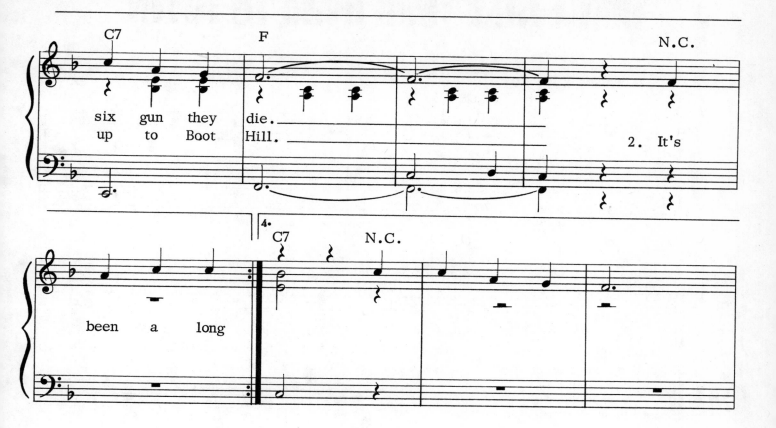

six   gun   they   die.____
up   to   Boot   Hill.____   2. It's

been   a   long

3. *Walk up to the fence there and look at the view,*
   That's where they were hanging 1882.
   It's easy to see where the brave men have died,
   Rope marks on the old tree are now petrified.

4. *At night when the moon shines so far away,*
   It gets mighty lonesome looking down on
      the grave.
   There lies Billie Clanton never wanted to kill,
   But he's there with the guilty way up on
      Boot Hill.

Note: In 1881, Billie Clanton—along with Tom McLowery and Frank McLowery—was shot down on the streets of Tombstone by Wyatt Earp and his deputies. Just before his death, Clanton called to Doc Holliday, "Don't shoot me. I don't want to fight."

DON'T TAKE YOUR GUNS TO TOWN

Moderately

Johnny Cash

1. A young cow-boy named Bil-ly Joe grew rest-less on the farm. A boy filled with wan-der-lust, who real-ly meant no harm. He changed his clothes and shined his boots and combed his dark hair

laughed and kissed his Mom and said: "Your Bil-ly Joe's a man. I can shoot as quick and straight as an-y-bod-y can. But I would-n't shoot with-out a cause; I'd gun no-bod-y

down,   And his   moth-er   cried as   he walked out:
down."   But she   cried a - gain as he   rode   a - way: }"Don't take your guns to

town,   son;   Leave your guns   at   home, Bill; Don't   take   your   guns   to

1. 2. 3. 4. *a tempo*   *5.*

town." _____   2. He   town." _____

3. He sang a song as on he rode, his guns hung
   at his hips.
He rode into a cattle town, a smile upon his lips.
He stopped and walked into a bar and laid
   his money down,
But his mother's words echoed again:
   "Don't take your guns to town, son;
Leave your guns at home, Bill; don't take your
   guns to town."

4. He drank his first strong liquor then to calm his
   shaking hand,
And tried to tell himself at last he had
   become a man.
A dusty cowpoke at his side began to laugh
   him down.

And he heard again his mother's words:
   "Don't take your guns to town, son;
Leave your guns at home, Bill; don't take your
   guns to town."

5. Bill was raged and Billy Joe reached for his
   gun to draw.
But the stranger drew his gun and fired before
   he even saw.
As Billy Joe fell to the floor the crowd all
   gathered 'round
And wondered at his final words:
   "Don't take your guns to town, son;
Leave your guns at home, Bill; don't take your
   guns to town."

COME IN, STRANGER

Moderately

Johnny Cash

She said: "Come in, stran-ger, it's good to have you home. I hur-ried thru 'cause I knew it was you when I saw your dog wag-gin' his tail. Hon-ey, why didn't you let me know by mail?__ You've been gone so long."__ She said:

"Come in, stran-ger, I know you're wea-ry from all___ the
"Come in, stran-ger, Oh, how I need you when you're

miles. Just sit right there in your eas - y chair___ and
gone. I walk the floor and I watch the door and when I

tell me all a - bout the plac - es you've been, how
lie a - wake and wonder where you can be, how I'd

long it'll be___ be - fore you leave a - gain.___ I
give an - y - thing to have you here with me. I get so

I'D STILL BE THERE

Johnny Cash and Johnny Horton

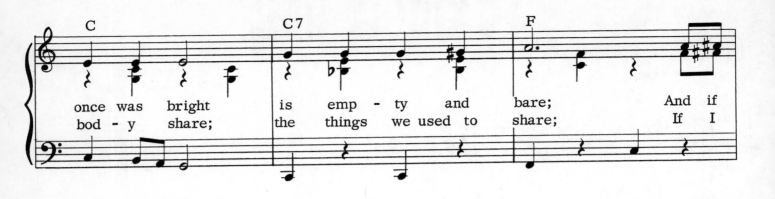

once was bright is emp-ty and bare; And if
bod-y share; the things we used to share; If I

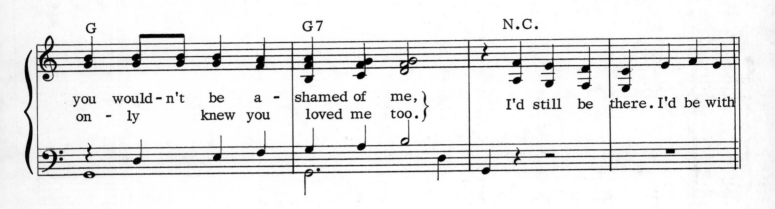

you would-n't be a-shamed of me, }
on-ly knew you loved me too. } I'd still be there. I'd be with

you,_____ where I be-long,_____

And noth-ing they could do or say could

make me think it's wrong. If all the love that

made you mine, could make you still care,

I'd be by your side, I'd still be

1. there._____

2. there._____

I STILL MISS SOMEONE

2. I go out on a party
   And look for a little fun.
   But I find a darkened corner
   'Cause I still miss someone.

3. I wonder if she's sorry
   For leaving what we'd begun.
   There's someone for me somewhere,
   And I still miss someone.

JACKSON

Fast 2

Billy Edd Wheeler and Gaby Rogers

1. We got mar-ried in a fe-ver, Hot-ter than a
go on down to Jack-son, Go a-head and

pep-per sprout; We've been talk-in' 'bout
wreck your health; Go play your

Jack-son, Ev-er since the fire went out.
talk-in' man, Make a big fool of your-self.

3. When I breeze into that city,
   I'll bet people gonna stop and bow.
   All them women gonna make me
   Teach 'em they don't know how.
   I'm goin' to Jackson,
   Turn-a loose of my coat.
   Yeah, I'm goin' to Jackson,
   "Goodbye," that's all she wrote.

4. When they laugh at you in Jackson,
   Dancin' on the pony keg;
   Then I'll lead you 'round town like a
      scalded hound,
   With your tail tucked between your legs.

So go on down to Jackson,
You big talkin' man;
I'll be waitin' in Jackson,
Behind my Japan fan.

5. We got married in a fever,
   Hotter than a pepper sprout.
   We've been talkin' 'bout Jackson,
   Ever since the fire went out.
   I'm goin' to Jackson,
   And that's a fact.
   Yeah, I'm goin' to Jackson,
   Ain't never comin' back.

GIVE MY LOVE TO ROSE

Moderately

Johnny Cash

Give my love to Rose, please, won't you, Mis - ter?

Take her all my mon - ey; tell her: buy some pret - ty clothes.

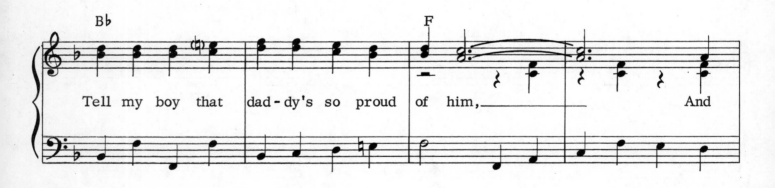

Tell my boy that dad - dy's so proud of him, And

don't for - get to give my love to Rose." 2."Won't-cha

TENNESSEE FLAT TOP BOX

Moderately fast

Johnny Cash

Aus - tin,_____ We're slip - pin' 'way from home and put - tin'
nine - ty,_____ Were snap - pin' fin - gers, tap - pin' toes and

jew - el - ry in hock; To take the trip, to go and
beg - gin' him don't stop; they were hyp - no - tized, and fas - ci -

lis - ten_____ To the lit - tle dark - haired boy that played the
na - ted_____ By the lit - tle dark - haired boy that played the

Ten - nes - see flat - top box. And he would play:

3. *Then one day he was gone*
   And no one ever saw him 'round ;
   He vanished like the breeze
   And they forgot him in the little town.
   And all the girls still dreamed about him,
   And they hung around the cabaret until the
      doors were locked ;
   And then one day, on the hit parade
   Was a little dark haired boy that played a
   Tennessee flat top box, And he would play:

I GOT STRIPES

New words and music by Johnny Cash and Charlie Williams.
Based on a song collected, adapted and arranged by John
A. and Alan Lomax

138

Thurs-day they said "guilt-y" and the judge's gav-el fell.
Thurs-day, Lord, I begged them not to knock me down a-gain.

I got stripes, stripes a-round my shoul-ders. I got chains, chains a-round my feet. I got stripes, stripes a-round my shoul-ders, And them chains, them chains, they're 'bout to drag me down. 2. On a down.

3. *On a Monday my mama come to see me.*
   On a Tuesday they caught me with a file.
   On a Wednesday I'm down in solitary.
   On a Thursday, Lord, I start on bread and
      water for a while. (To Chorus.)

FOLSOM PRISON BLUES

Moderately

Johnny Cash

3. I bet there's rich folks eatin' in a fancy
   dining car.
   They're prob'ly drinkin' coffee and smokin'
   big cigars,
   But I know I had it comin', I know I can't be free,
   But those people keep a-movin', and that's
   what tortures me.

4. Well, if they freed me from this prison, if that
   railroad train was mine,
   I bet I'd move on over a little farther down
   the line,
   Far from Folsom Prison, that's where I want
   to stay,
   And I'd let that lonesome whistle blow my
   blues away.

I WALK THE LINE

Johnny Cash

3. As sure as night is dark and day is light,
   I keep you on my mind both day and night.
   And happiness I've known proves that it's right.
   Because you're mine I walk the line.

4. You've got a way to keep me on your side.
   You give me cause for love that I can't hide.

For you I know I'd even try to turn the tide.
Because you're mine I walk the line.

5. I keep a close watch on this heart of mine,
   I keep my eyes wide open all the time.
   I keep the ends out for the tie that binds.
   Because you're mine I walk the line.

SHANTYTOWN

Johnny Cash and June Carter

Moderately

I live down in Shan-ty-town,___ where chick-en's twen-ty cents a pound.___ And if you live on___ such sol-id ground,___

ANOTHER SONG TO SING

Johnny Cash

1. Do they ask you where I am or where I've been,
Do they ev - er say "Where is the lone - ly
friend"_____
Is my name whis - pered

2. Do you tell them I was wild - er than the wind,
Do you re - mem - ber that I need - ed lots of
friends,_____
And at oth - er times I'd

sit down with and talk;
by those gone be - fore;

And some-
At the

bod - y might ap - pre - ci - ate the flow - ers I could
top of the ti - ni - est hill I can feel like I'm a

bring, so
king, and

there's al - ways an - oth - er song to

1.
sing.

2.
sing.

PICKIN' TIME

Moderately

Johnny Cash

1. I got cot-ton in the bot-tom land.___ It's up and growin' and I got a good stand.___ My good wife and them kids of mine,___ Gon-na get new shoes___ come pick-in' time,___

2. Ev-'ry night when I go to bed,___ I thank the Lord that my kids are fed.___ They live on beans eight days in nine,___ But I get 'em fat___ come pick-in' time,___

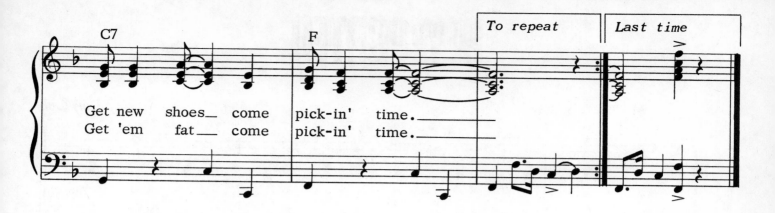

Get new shoes__ come pick-in' time.__

Get 'em fat__ come pick-in' time.__

3. The corn is yellow and the beans are high.
   The sun is hot in the summer sky.
   The work is hard till layin' by,
   Layin' by till pickin' time,
   Layin' by till pickin' time.

4. It's hard to see by the coal oil light,
   And I turn it off pretty early at night.
   'Cause a jug of coal oil costs a dime,
   But I stay up late come pickin' time,
   Stay up late come pickin' time.

5. My old wagon barely gets me to town.
   I patched the wheels and I watered 'em down.
   Keep her in shape so she'll be fine
   To haul my cotton come pickin' time,
   Haul my cotton come pickin' time.

6. Last Sunday morning when they passed the hat,
   It was still nearly empty back where I sat.
   But the preacher smiled and said, "That's fine;
   The Lord'll wait till pickin' time,
   The Lord'll wait till pickin' time."

HEY, PORTER

Moderately fast

Johnny Cash

152

neer to slow it down; or bet-ter still, just
neer to ring his bell; And ask ev-'ry-bod-y that

stop the train 'cause I want to look a - round.
ain't a sleep to stand right up and yell. 2. Hey,

Repeat and fade

3. Hey, Porter! Hey, Porter! It's getting
    light outside.
  This old train is puffing smoke and I have to
    strain my eyes.
  But ask that engineer if he will blow his
    whistle please,
  'Cause I smell frost on cotton leaves, and I smell
    that Southern breeze.

4. Hey, Porter! Hey, Porter! Please get my
    boys for me
  I need nobody to tell me now that we're
    in Tennessee.

Go tell that engineer to make that lonesome
    whistle scream.
We're not so far from home so take it easy
    on the steam.

5. Hey, Porter! Hey, Porter! Please open up
    my door.
  When they stop this train I'm gonna get off
    first 'cause I can't wait no more.
  Tell that engineer I say, "Thanks a lot.
    I didn't mind the fare.
  I'm gonna set my feet on Southern soil and
    breathe that Southern air."

AS LONG AS THE GRASS SHALL GROW

Quickly, but expressively

Peter La Farge

155

(Spoken)
The Senecas are an Indian tribe,
of the Iroquois nation,
Down on the New York-Pennsylvania line,
You'll find their reservation,
After the U.S. revolution,
Cornplanter was a chief,
He told the tribe these men they could trust
That was his true belief,
He went down to Independence Hall,
And there was a treaty signed,
That promised peace with the U.S.A.
And Indian rights combined,
George Washington gave his signature,
The Government gave its hand,
They said that now and forever more,
This was Indian land.

(To Chorus) *As long as the moon shall rise, etc.*
(Spoken)
On the Seneca reservation,
There is much sadness now,
Washington's treaty has been broken,
And there is no hope, no how,
Across the Allegheny River,
They're throwing up a dam,
It will flood the Indian country,
A proud day for Uncle Sam,
It has broke the ancient treaty
With a politician's grin,
It will down the Indians' graveyards,
Cornplanter can you swim?
The Earth is Mother to the Senecas,
They're trampling sacred ground,
Change the mint green earth to black mud flats,
As honor hobbles down . . .

(To Chorus)
(Spoken)
The Iroquois Indians used to rule,
From Canada way south,
But no one fears the Indians now,
And smiles the liar's mouth,
The Senecas hired an expert,
To figure another site,
But the great good army engineers,
Said that he had no right,
Although he showed them another plan,
And showed them another way,
They laughed in his face and said no deal,
Kinuza dam is here to stay,
Congress turned the Indians down
Brushed off the Indians' plea,
So the Senecas have renamed the dam,
They call it lake perfidy . . .

(To Chorus)
(Spoken)
Washington, Adams and Kennedy,
Now hear their pledges ring,
The treaties are safe, we'll keep our word,
But what is that gurgling?
It's the back water from perfidy lake
It's rising all the time,
Over the homes and over the fields,
Over the promises fine,
No boats will sail on lake perfidy,
In winter it will fill,
In summer it will be a swamp,
And all the fish will kill,
But the Government of the U.S.A.,
Has corrected George's vow,
The father of our country must be wrong,
What's an Indian, anyhow . . .

THE TALKING LEAVES

Johnny Cash

157

winters were sixteen; silent tongue -- spirit
clean. He walked at his father's side
a - cross the smoking bat-tle-ground, Where red
had died. The wind had scat-tered a-round snow white leaves
and white men lay all around. So many men here
up-on the ground. Not leaves

From where come such snow white leaves with such
   strange marks upon the squares?
Not even the wise owl could put them there—so
   strange, these snow white leaves."
His father, shielding his concern, resenting the
   knowledge Sequoia yearned,
Crumbled the snow white leaves,
He said, "When I explain, then it's done.
   These are talking leaves, my son.
The white man's talking leaves.
The white man takes a berry of black and red, and
   an eagle's feather from the eaglet's bed.
And he makes bird track marks.
And the marks on the leaves, they say, carry
   messages to his brother far away.
And his brother knows what's in his heart.
They see these marks and they understand the truth
   in the heart of the far-off man.

The enemies can't hear them."
Said Sequoia's father, "Son, they weave bad
   medicine on these talking leaves.
Leave such things to them."
Then, Sequoia, walking lightly, followed his father
   quietly. But so amazed was he.
If the white man talks on leaves, why not
   the Cherokee?
Banished from his father's gaze, Sequoia went
   from place to place.
But he could not forget.
Year after year, he worked on and on.
Till finally he cut into stone the Cherokee alphabet.
Sequoia's hair, by now, was white. His eyes began
   to lose their light.
But he taught all who would believe that the
   Indian's thoughts could be written down.
And he left us these talking leaves.

159

FIVE FEET HIGH AND RISING

Moderately

Johnny Cash

1. How high is the wa - ter, Ma - ma? Two feet high and ris - ing. How high is the wa - ter, Pa - pa? She said it's two feet high and ris - ing. But we can make it to the road in a
2. How high is the wa - ter, Ma - ma? Three feet high and ris - ing. How high is the wa - ter, Pa - pa? She said it's three feet high and ris - ing. Well, the hives are gone, I

home made boat, 'cause that's the | on - ly thing we got | left that'll float. It's
lost my bees; | chick-ens are sleep-in' in the wil - low trees.

al - ready o - ver all the wheat and oats. | Two feet high and ris - ing.
Cows in wa-ter up past their knees. | Three feet high and ris - ing.

ris - ing. Well, it's | five feet high and | ris - ing.

3. How high is the water, Mama? Four feet high
   and rising.
   How high is the water, Papa? She said it's
   four feet high and rising.
   Hey, come look through the window pane;
   the bus is comin' gonna take us to the train.
   Looks like we'll be blessed with a little more rain.
   Four feet high and rising.

4. How high is the water, Mama? Five feet high
   and rising.
   How high is the water, Papa? She said it's
   five feet high and rising.
   Well, the rails are washed out north of town;
   we gotta head for higher ground.
   We can't come back till the water goes down.
   Five feet high and rising;
   Well, it's five feet high and rising.

UNDERSTAND YOUR MAN

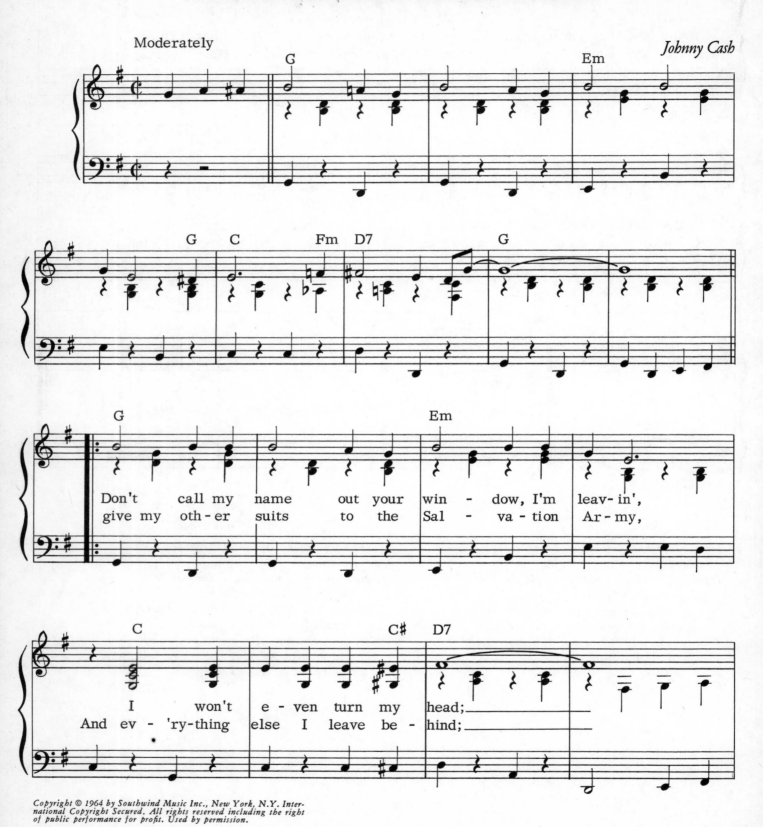

Moderately

Johnny Cash

Don't call my name out your win - dow, I'm leav-in',
give my oth-er suits to the Sal - va-tion Ar-my,

I won't e - ven turn my head;____
And ev-'ry-thing else I leave be - hind;____

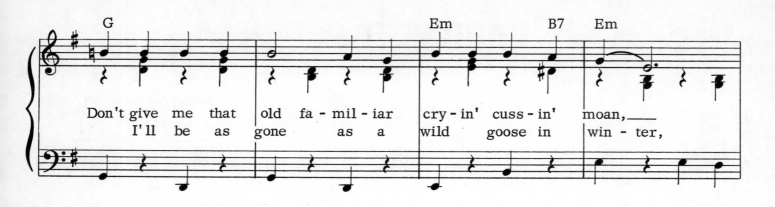

Repeat and fade

HAPPINESS IS YOU

Moderately

Johnny Cash and June Carter

1. Way down the mountain, I chased a moonbeam, On the beach I built sand castles
2. I tried to doubt you, and live without you, Tried to deny that I love you like I

too; _____ My moon - beams fad - ed,_____

do; _____ But I re - al - ize now,_____

_____ My cas - tles tum - bled,_____ You'll

And I'll ad - mit it,_____

All of this was mean - ing - less, 'cause

al - ways be a part of me, 'cause hap - pi - ness is

you._____ No more chas - in'

moon - beams, or catch - in' fall - ing stars;

CRY, CRY, CRY

Moderately

Johnny Cash

Ev-'ry bod-y know where you go when the sun goes down. I think you on-ly live to see the lights up-town. I wast-ed my time when I would try, try,

RUN SOFTLY, BLUE RIVER

Johnny Cash

BIG RIVER

Boogie-Woogie

Johnny Cash

Now, I taught the weep-ing wil-low how to cry,_____ And I showed the clouds how to cov-er up a clear blue sky. And the

tears that I cried for that wom-an____ are gon-na flood you, Big

Riv-er. Then I'm gon-na sit right here un-til I

die. 2. I die.

2. I met her accidentally in St. Paul (Minnesota).
   And it tore me up ev'ry time I heard her drawl,
      Southern drawl.
   Then I heard my dream was back downstream
      cavortin' in Davenport,
   And I followed you, Big River, when you called.

3. Then you took me to St. Louis later on
      (down the river).
   A freighter said she's been here but she's gone,
      boy, she's gone.
   I found her trail in Memphis, but she just
      walked up the block.
   She raised a few eyebrows and then she went
      on down alone.

4. Now, won't you batter down by Baton Rouge,
      River Queen, roll it on.
   Take that woman on down to New Orleans,
      New Orleans.
   Go on, I've had enough; dump my blues down
      in the gulf.
   She loves you, Big River, more than me.

5. Now, I taught the weeping willow how to cry,
   And I showed the clouds how to cover up a
      clear blue sky.
   And the tears that I cried for that woman are
      gonna flood you, Big River.
   Then I'm gonna sit right here until I die.

HARDIN WOULDN'T RUN

Johnny Cash

3. He rode in like the Texas wind, took the
    Eastbound train,
    Goin', goin' with Jane Bowen, till the law
    men caught up.
    "So long, Janie. Chin up. I'll be back again."

4. Off he went to Huntsville prison,
    "So long, Jane," he cried.
    Fifteen years she waited, till her heart broke
    and she died,
    And she left that bad land to wait up in the sky.

5. Free at last, the payin' past for all the wrong
    he did.
    First free air they let him breathe since he
    was a kid.
    So let him come and let him go, and let him
    deal and bid.

6. Near the border in El Paso "Lawyer" reads
    the sign,
    But you won't find him there for bus'ness ev'ry

day at nine.
    For bus'ness is real bad, one client's all he had
    in quite a long time.

7. Then Sheriff Selman's boy broke into Wes's
    woman's place.
    Up she jumped and pistol whipped him, kicked
    him in the face.
    And John Selman demands revenge for
    this disgrace.

8. You can see her ev'ry night by candlelight at
    Hardin's fav'rite bar.
    She'd be hangin' on his arm, and very late
    they'd leave there,
    Headin' for the goose hair, glad it wasn't far.

9. Thru the swingin' door John Selman came with
    blazin' gun.
    Wes Hardin chug-a-luggin' red eye, got him in
    the back of the head.
    John Wesley Hardin fell dead, cause Hardin
    wouldn't run.

THE BIG BATTLE

Johnny Cash

Moderately

1. I

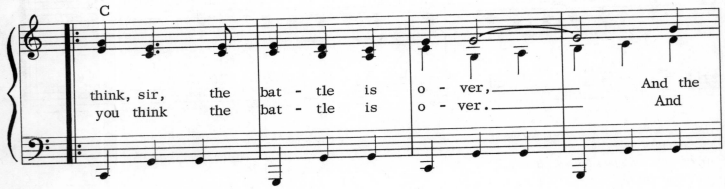

think, sir,   the   bat - tle   is   o - ver,_____   And the
you think   the   bat - tle   is   o - ver._____   And

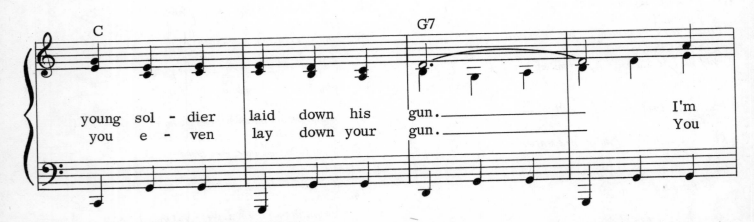

young sol - dier   laid   down   his   gun._____   I'm
you e - ven   lay   down   your   gun._____   You

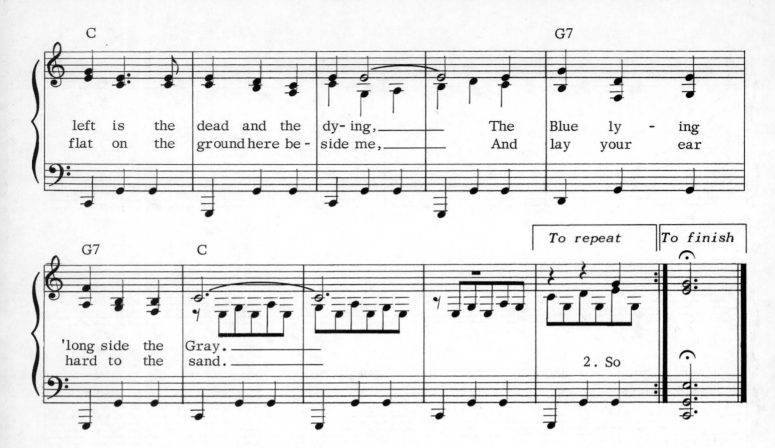

left is the dead and the dy- ing,_____ The Blue ly - ing
flat on the ground here be- side me,_____ And lay your ear

To repeat | To finish

'long side the Gray._____
hard to the sand._____

2. So

3. (Can) you hear the deafening rumble?
   Can you feel the trembling ground?
   It's not just the horses and wagons
   That make such a deafening sound.
   For ev'ry shot fired has an echo,
   And ev'ry man killed wanted life.
   —There lies your friend Jim McKenney.
   Can you take the news to his wife?

4. (—) No, son, the battle's not over.
   You'll see that it's only begun.
   The rest of the battle will cover
   The part that has blackened the sun.
   The fight yet to come's not with cannon,
   Nor will the fight be hand to hand.
   —No one will regroup the forces;
   No charge will a gen'ral command.

5. (The) battle will rage in the bosom
   of mother and sweetheart and wife.
   —Brother and sister and daughter
   Will grieve for the rest of their lives.
   Now go ahead, rise from your cover.
   Be thankful that God let you live.
   —Go fight the rest of the battle
   For those who gave all they could give.

6. (I) see, sir, the battle's not over.
   The battle has only begun.
   The rest of the battle will cover
   This part that has blackened the sun.
   For tho' there's no sound of the cannon
   And tho' there's no smoke in the sky,
   I'm dropping the gun and the saber,
   And ready for battle am I.

WRECK OF THE OLD NINETY-SEVEN

Quickly

Johnny Cash, B. Johnson, W. Blake

1. Well, they
give him his or - ders at Mon - roe, Vir -
might - y rough road from Lynch - burg to

gin - ia, say - in': "Steve, you're way be - hind
Dan - ville with a line on a three mile

time. This is not Thir - ty
grade. It was on that

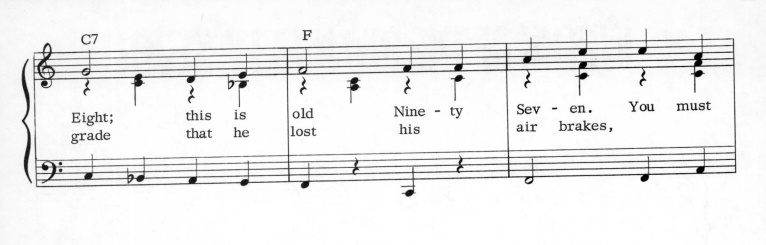

3. Then a telegram come to Washington station
   And this is how it read:
   "Oh that brave engineer that run old
   Ninety-Seven,
   He's a lying in old Danville dead."

4. So now all you ladies you better take a warning
   From this time on and learn:
   Never speak harsh words to your true
   lovin' husband;
   He may leave you and never return.

WHEN PAPA PLAYED THE DOBRO

Johnny Cash

184

could-n't   pay   the   fee.   But   when   the   go - in'
oth - er   play - ers   did.   Why   the   gui - tar's   reso-

got   too   bad,   to   ease   his   mis - er - y,
na - tor   was   a   gal - lon   buck - et   lead.   But

G   G7
Pa - pa   played   the   do - bro   this - a   way: _____
Pa - pa   played   the   do - bro   this - a   way: _____

C7   F   C   F   F   C   F
___   And   he'd   go:

3. *Well, now that Papa's gone away, it's hanging*
   by the flue.
   The top of it's rusted and the strings are
   rusty too.
   It won't ever sound the way that it did when
   it was new.
   When Papa played the dobro this-a way:
   And he'd go:

LUTHER'S BOOGIE

Fast Boogie Tempo

Johnny Cash

just a plain ol' hill - bill - y band with a plain ol' coun - try
did our best to en - ter - tain ev - 'ry - where we'd

style;
go;

We nev - er played the kind____
We'd near - ly wear our fin -

— of songs____ that would drive an - y bod - y wild;____
gers off, just to give the folks a show;____

We played a rail-road song with a stomp-in' beat,___ we played a
We played the jump-in' jive to make 'em get in the groove,___ we played the

blues song, kind-a slow and sweet;___ But the thing that knocked___ them
sad songs, real slow and sweet;___ But the on-ly thing___ that'd

off-a their feet was
make 'em move was
ooh we-e When

Luth-er played the Boo-gie Woo-gie Luth-er played the Boo-gie Woo-gie.

Luth-er played the Boo-gie in the stran - gest

kind of way. Well, we

way. (spoken:) How dear Luther

played the Boogie strange!

NO, NO, NO

Moderately

Johnny Cash

(Boy): I'm a

poor boy from the farm__ land, Your fa - ther is a wealth - y
dad - dy brings you silk to sew from the fin - est shops in

sail - in' man.   If I asked you for your__ hand
To - ky - o. He told you to turn me down, I know,__ but

would you tell me
don't say   } no,   oh,   no,__ no,__ no.__

3. (Boy) *I can't give you anything,*
I can't afford a wedding ring,
A present that I'd like to bring.
But oh, I love you so, oh, don't say no.

(Girl) *My Daddy's three days out to sea,*
And he would turn me across his knee,
If he knew you were kissing me.
But I can't let you go,
Oh, no, no, no, oh,
(Both) *No, no, no.*

OH, WHAT A GOOD THING WE HAD

Lively

Johnny Cash and June Carter

good thing we had.

(Girl): Drive - ins and pic - nics and ev - 'ry day___ was
Hap - pi - ness and laugh - ter, we found ev - 'ry-thing we

Sat - ur-day,___
were af - ter,___ Oh, what a good thing we had, gone

bad, Oh, what a good thing we had.

YOU'LL BE ALL RIGHT

Johnny Cash and June Carter

cry just a lit - tle bit, And die just a lit - tle bit, And then you'll be all

To repeat right.

To finish right.

2. Why, don't you know,
   it wasn't long ago,
   your honey bee
   was queen of my bee tree.
   But then away she flew,
   and took my honey to you.
   You cry just a little bit,
   and die just a little bit,
   and then you'll be all right.

3. Well, I pity you;
   I know what you're going through.
   You saw your queen bee fly;
   your honeycomb went dry.
   But if you keep pushin' on,
   you won't care if she's gone.
   You cry just a little bit,
   and die just a little bit,
   and then you'll be all right.

SING IT PRETTY, SUE

Johnny Cash

prop'r - ty, so I re - lease my claim to you; Go
pic - tures like an - y fan would do; And

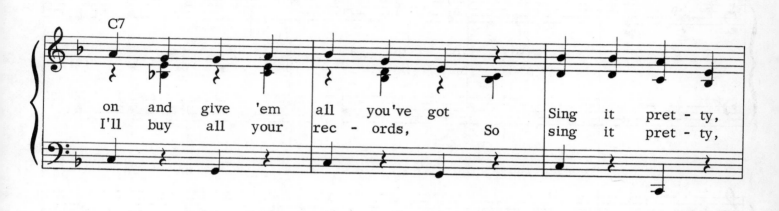

on and give 'em all you've got Sing it pret - ty,
I'll buy all your rec - ords, So sing it pret - ty,

Sue. _____
Sue. _____
But I can't take just
I won't ev - er

part of you and give the world a half, So
tell a soul that we have ev - er met, I'll

OLD APACHE SQUAW

Moderately

Johnny Cash

Old A - pach - e
Old A - pach - e

squaw,
squaw,

How man - y long, lean years you saw?___
How man - y hun - gry kids you saw?___

How man - y bit - ter win - ter nights,___
How man - y blood - y war - ri - ors,___

Shiv-'rin' in a cold tee-
Run - nin' to the

pee,
sea,

Shiv-'rin' in a cold tee - pee?
Flee - in' to the

sea?   Well, now   they tell me that you saw Co - chise, when

he made his last stand; He said, "The next white man that

sees my face is gon - na   be a dead white man."

Old A - pach - e squaw, How man - y bro - ken

FORTY SHADES OF GREEN

Johnny Cash

Moderately, with expression

close my eyes and pic - ture the em - 'rald of the sea.
wish that I could spend an hour at Dub - lin's churn - ing surf.

From the fish - ing boats at Din - gle, to the shores of Dun - a - dee.
I'd love to watch the farm - ers drain the bogs and spade the turf.

I miss the Riv - er
To see a - gain the

YOU REMEMBERED ME

Moderately bright

Johnny Cash

1. You were young___ and need-ed love,___ and I was wild___ and
2. I be-lieved___ that prom-is-es___ were made to break___ a-

free. But ev-'ry time you said a prayer,___ you
part. But ev-'ry time I said broke a vow,___ I

said a prayer____ for me.

al-ways broke____ your heart. So By the ring____ up-

here's to you;____ God

on your hand____ we vowed fi-del - i - ty.}

bless you now____ where ev - er you____ may be.}

There were times____ when I for-got;____ but you re-mem - bered

me. You re-mem - bered on - ly that

THE WHIRL AND THE SUCK

Johnny Cash

AUSTIN PRISON

Moderately

Johnny Cash

1. They had a
war-rant out for me all o-ver the coun-try.____
steel grey eyes were blaz-in' when__ he saw me,____
And I was try-in' to beat the raps in I-da-
His hand was on his gun when he rode

3. Well, he tied me with a blow iron the
      next mornin',
   and he had me deep in Texas the next day.
   A crazy, screamin' lynch mob waited in the
      streets of Austin,
   but he put me in the jailhouse, and he threw
      away the key.

4. A jury found me guilty three months later,
   twelve evil men with murder in their eyes.
   They even took me out and said,

   "Now, show us where you killed her!"
   And that wicked judge said,
      "Now I hereby sentence you to die."

5. But here I am quite away from Austin Prison;
   my friend, the jailer, handed me a file.
   Now all I want between me and there are a
      lot of friendly people,
   and miles and miles and miles and miles
      and miles and miles and miles.

A BOY NAMED SUE

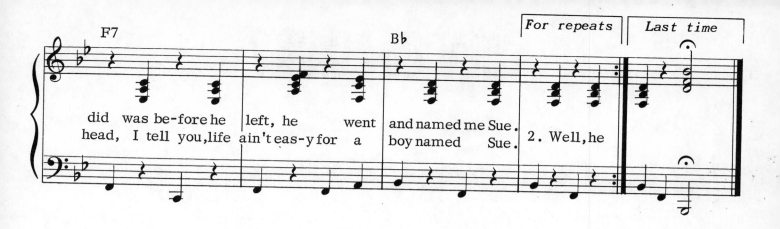

F7   Bb   For repeats | Last time

did was be-fore he   left, he   went and named me Sue.   2. Well, he
head, I tell you, life ain't eas-y for a   boy named   Sue.

3. (Well,) I grew up quick and I grew up mean.
   My fist got hard and my wits got keen.
   Roamed from town to town to hide my shame,
   but I made me a vow to the moon and stars,
   I'd search the honky tonks and bars and kill
   that man that give me that awful name.

4. But it was Gatlinburg in mid July and I had
   just hit town and my throat was dry.
   I'd thought I'd stop and have myself a brew.
   At an old saloon on a street of mud
   And at a table dealing stud sat the dirty,
   mangy dog that named me Sue.

5. Well I knew that snake was my own sweet dad
   from a worn-out picture that my mother had.
   And I know that scar on his cheek and his evil eye.
   He was big and bent and gray and old
   And I looked at him and my blood ran cold,
   and I said, "My name is Sue. How do you do.

   Now you're gonna die." Yeah, that's what
   I told him.

6. Well I hit him right between the eyes and he
   went down, but to my surprise he come up
   with a knife
   And cut off a piece of my ear. But I busted a
   chair right across his teeth. And we
   crashed through
   The wall and into the street kicking and
   a-gouging in the mud and the blood
   and the beer.

7. I tell you I've fought tougher men but I really
   can't remember when.

He kicked like a mule and he bit like a
   crocodile. I heard him laughin' and then
   I heard him cussin',
He went for his gun and I pulled mine first.
   He stood there looking at me and I saw
   him smile,

8. And he said, "Son, this world is rough and if
   a man's gonna make it, he's gotta be tough
   And I know I wouldn't be there to help you
   along. So I give you that name and I
   said 'Goodbye,'
   I knew you'd have to get tough or die. And it's
   that name that helped to make you strong.

9. Yeah," he said, "now you have just fought one
   helluva fight, and I know you hate me
   and you've
   Got the right to kill me now and I wouldn't
   blame you if you do. But you ought
   to thank me
   Before I die for the gravel in your guts and the
   spit in your eye because I'm the __ __ __ __
   That named you Sue."

   Yeah, what could I do? What could I do?

10. I got all choked up and I threw down my gun.
    Called him a pa and he called me a son,
    And I come away with a different point of view.
    And I think about him now and then.
    Every time I tried, every time I win and if I
    ever have a son I think I am gonna name him
    Bill or George—anything but Sue.

WHAT DO I CARE?

Johnny Cash

218

Chorus:

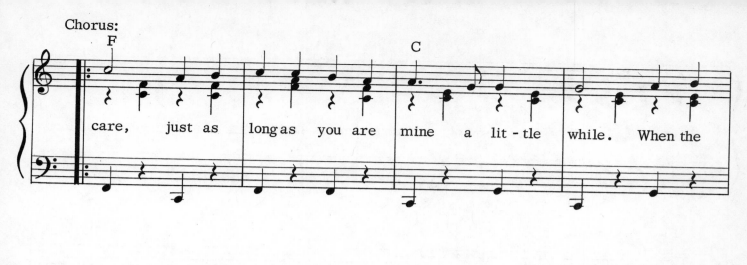

care, just as long as you are mine a lit-tle while. When the

road was long and wea - ry you gave me a few good miles. What do I

care if I miss a goal be - cause I make a slip? I'll

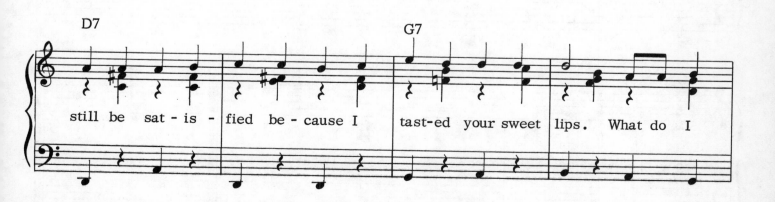

still be sat - is - fied be - cause I tast-ed your sweet lips. What do I

care if I nev-er have much mon-ey,_____ And some

times my ta - ble looks a lit - tle bare?_____

An - y - thing that I may miss is made up

for each time we kiss. You love me and I love

you, so what do I care?_____ What do I

SO DOGGONE LONESOME

Moderately bright

Johnny Cash

1. I do my best to hide this low-down feel-in'.
2. Time stands still when you're a-wait-in'.

I try to make be-lieve there's noth-ing wrong.
Some-times I think my heart is stop-pin' too.

But they're al-ways ask-in' me a-bout you, dar-lin',
One lone-ly hour seems for-ev-er.

And it hurts me so to tell 'em that you're
Six - ty min - utes more a - wait - in' for

gone._____ If they ask me I guess I'd be de -
you._____ But I guess I'll keep wait - in' till you're

ny - in',_____ That I've been un - hap - py all a -
with me._____ 'Cause I be - lieve that lov - in' you is

lone._____ But if they heard my heart, they'd hear it
right._____ But I don't care if the sun don't rise to -

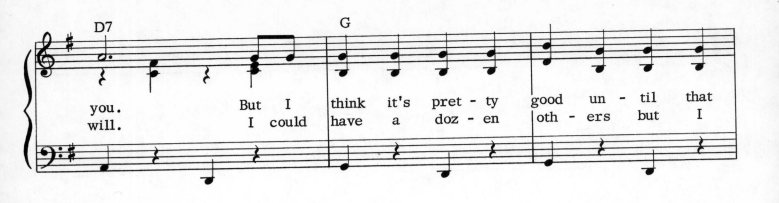

you.   But I   think   it's   pret - ty   good   un - til   that

will.   I could   have   a   doz - en   oth - ers   but   I

moon   comes   shin - in'   through,   And   then   I   get   so

know   I'd   love   you   still,   'Cause   I   get   so

dog - gone   lone-some.

dog - gone   lone-some.

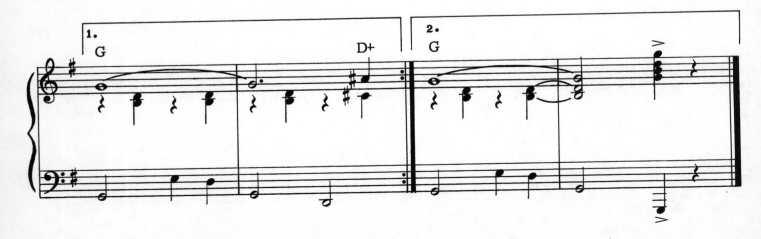

JOHNNY CASH:

Notes for albums *Johnny Cash
at Folsom Prison*
and *Bob Dylan: Nashville Skyline*

FOLSOM PRISON BLUES

for "Johnny Cash at Folsom Prison"

The culture of a thousand years is shattered with the clanging of the cell door behind you. Life outside behind you immediately becomes unreal. You begin to not care that it exists. All you have with you in the cell is your bare animal instincts.

I speak partly from experience. I have been behind bars a few times. Sometimes of my own volition—sometimes involuntarily. Each time, I felt the same feeling of kinship with my fellow prisoners.

Behind the bars, locked out from "society," you're being rehabilitated, corrected, re-briefed, re-educated on life itself, without your having the opportunity of really reliving it. You're the object of a widely planned program combining isolation, punishment, training, briefing, etc., designed to make you sorry for your mistakes, to re-enlighten you on what you should and shouldn't do outside, so that when you're released, if you ever are, you can come out clean, to a world that's supposed to welcome you and forgive you.

Can it work??? "Hell no," you say. How could this torment possibly do anybody any good. . . . But then, why else are you locked in?

You sit on your cold, steel mattress and watch a cockroach crawl out from under the filthy commode, and you don't kill it. You envy the roach as you watch it crawl out under the cell door.

Down the cell block you hear a steel door open, then close. Like every other man that hears it, your first unconscious thought reaction is that it's someone coming to let you out, but you know it isn't.

You count the steel bars on the door so many times that you hate yourself for it. Your big accomplishment for the day is a mathematical deduction. You are positive of this, and only this: There are nine vertical, and sixteen horizontal bars on your door.

Down the hall another door opens and closes, then a guard walks by without looking at you, and on out another door.

"The son of a . . . . . ."

You'd like to say that you are waiting for something, but nothing ever happens. There is nothing to look forward to.

You make friends in the prison. You become one in a "clique" whose purpose is nothing. Nobody is richer or poorer than the other. The only way wealth is measured is by the amount of tobacco a man has, or "Duffy's Hay" as tobacco is called.

All of you have had the same things snuffed out of your lives. Everything it seems that makes a man a man: Women, money, a family, a job, the open road, the city, the country, ambition, power, success, failure—a million things.

Outside your cellblock is a wall. Outside that wall is another wall. It's twenty feet high, and its granite blocks go down another eight feet in the ground. You know you're here to stay, and for some reason, you'd like to stay alive—and not rot.

So for the fourth time I have done so in California. I brought my show to Folsom. Prisoners are the greatest audience that an entertainer can perform for. We bring them a ray of sunshine in their dungeon and they're not ashamed to respond, and show their appreciation. And after six years of talking, I finally found the man who would listen at Columbia Records. Bob Johnston believed me when I told him that a prison would be the place to record an album live.

Here's the proof. Listen closely to this album and you hear in the background the clanging of the doors, the shrill of the whistle, the shout of the men—even laughter from men who had forgotten how to laugh.

But mostly you'll feel the electricity and hear the single pulsation of two thousand heartbeats in men who have had their hearts torn out, as well as their minds, their nervous systems, and their souls.

Hear the sounds of the men, the convicts all brothers of mine—with the Folsom Prison Blues.

Johnny Cash, 1968

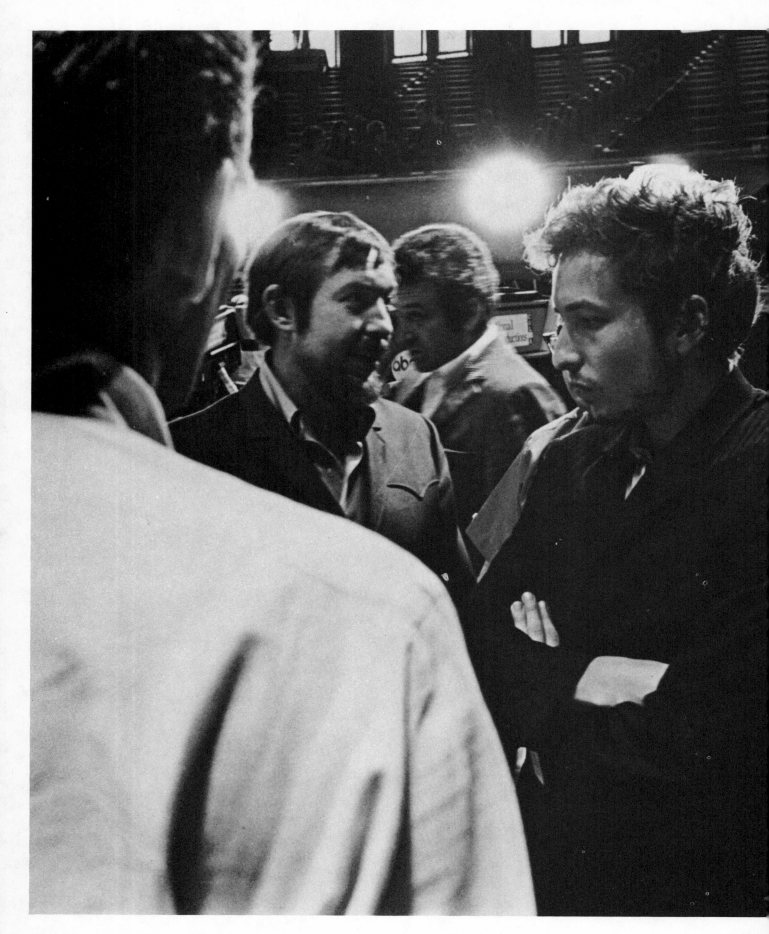

OF BOB DYLAN

for "Bob Dylan: Nashville Skyline"

There are those who do not imitate,
Who cannot imitate
But then there are those who emulate
At times, to expand further the light
Of an original glow.

    Knowing that to imitate the living
    Is mockery
    And to imitate the dead
    Is robbery
There are those
Who are beings complete unto themselves
Whole, undaunted—a source
    As leaves of grass, as stars,
    As mountains, alike, alike, alike
    Yet unalike
    Each is complete and contained
And as each unalike star shines
Each ray of light is forever gone
To leave way for a new ray
And a new ray, as from a fountain
Complete unto itself, full, flowing.
    So are some souls like stars
    And their words, works and songs
Like strong, quick flashes of light
From a brilliant, erupting cone.
    So where are your mountains
    To match some men?

This man can rhyme the tick of time
The edge of pain, the what of sane
And comprehend the good in men, the bad in men
    Can feel the hate of fight, the love of right
    And the creep of blight at the speed of light
The pain of dawn, the gone of gone
The end of friend, the end of end
By math of trend
    What grip to hold what he is told
    How long to hold, how strong to hold
    How much to hold of what is told.
And Know
    The yield of rend; the break of bend
    The scar of mend
    I'm proud to say that I know it.
    Here-in is a hell of a poet.
    And lots of other things
    And lots of other things.

Johnny Cash, 1969

PICKING WITH JOHNNY CASH

by Happy Traum

Most of the songs in this book can be described as "country songs," not because they are necessarily from a rural neighborhood, but because the rhythms and chord patterns create a traditional sound and feeling that has its roots in the American folk style. The guitar is of course the instrument which most typifies this style, and its sound is almost indispensable to country music. Listen to any of the songs — "I Walk The Line," "Folsom Prison," "Jackson," "A Boy Named Sue," — and you will hear the familiar *boom*-chick-a *boom*-chick-a rhythm setting the time as folk and country guitarists have been doing for generations.

This guitar style has many names. Woody Guthrie called it the "church lick," others call it the "scratch," and many name it after a singing group that first made that particular guitar sound famous — The Carter Family. (You can still see and hear Mother Maybelle Carter, one of the original trio, picking and singing on many of Johnny Cash's shows, and her singing daughter, June Carter, is married to Johnny Cash.) The Carter Family guitar style can be learned easily even by someone just starting the guitar, and it will certainly add to his enjoyment of these songs.

The Carter Family lick is based on a bass-chord bass-chord pattern usually played with a flat-pick, although some people prefer a thumb and forefinger combination instead. Here is how it goes:

Finger a chord — let's start with A.

1) Pluck down on your bass (5th or A) string, producing a sharp, clear tone. Use your thumb or flat pick.
2) Brush down (↓) across the three highest strings with your index finger or pick.
3) Brush up (↑) across the same three strings.

Repeat all three steps, this time using an alternate bass note (6th or 4th string).

Now do the whole thing again, this time saying: *boom* (bass)-chick (↓) a (↑); *boom*-chicka, *boom*-chicka . . .

That's all there is to it. Try it with different chords, experimenting to find the bass notes that sound best with the chord you are playing. Keep the rhythm good and steady — try not to slow down or speed up. Once you feel at home with this strum, try it with a song.

If you are playing in 3/4 time, the strum would be slightly different, although not more difficult to play: *boom*-chicka-chicka / *boom*-chicka-chicka (bass-down-up-down-up). Concentrate on getting a steady rhythm, with clean bass notes and sharp, clear chords.

Playing these songs on guitar will increase your enjoyment of them, partly because you will be approximating the sounds you hear on records, radio and TV, and partly because the guitar lends itself so beautifully to these songs. Its voice has become familiar to us through the years, and most of us have come to love it as an integral part of our heritage. It is also an easy instrument to pick up and play with a minimum of musical training.

Of course, even if you master these techniques perfectly, you will not sound like a Johnny Cash record. He is backed by a tight, professional group (The Tennessee Three) playing electric guitar, bass and drums behind his folky church lick. This group, and the sound it produces, has become almost as much a trademark for Johnny Cash as the famous voice itself. If you listen carefully, you will hear that the basis for this sound is still the traditional strum, but the guitar is set to make a sharp, metallic treble sound, and is played with short, precise "chops," the strings cut off almost before they have a chance to ring. The guitarist often plays chord inversions up the neck, which increases the sharp, treble sound. The bass and drums fill out the rest of the accompaniment in a similarly rhythmic way.

If you have an electric guitar, and are a little more advanced, you might try to get some of these sounds. If not, play the songs as well as you can, and you will have a fine time with them.

We have included below a page of chord diagrams for those who are unfamiliar with the chords in this book.

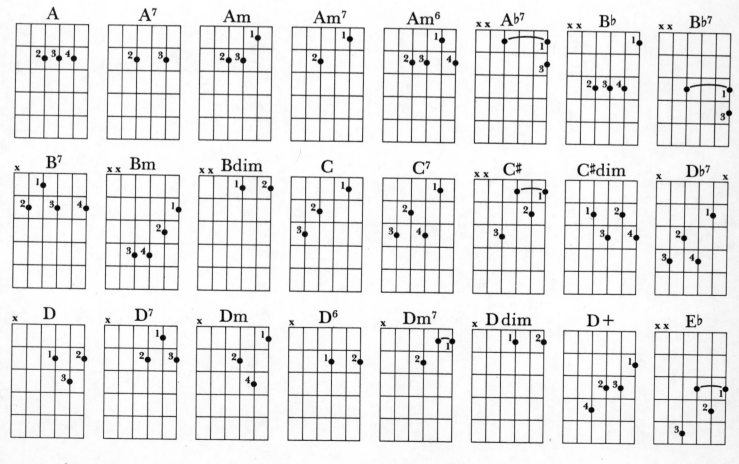

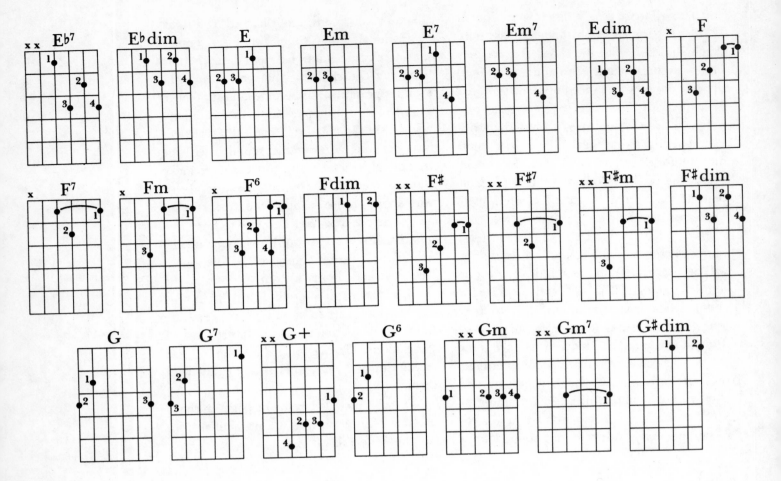

SELECTED DISCOGRAPHY

ORIGINAL GOLDEN HITS, VOL. 1
Sun Records (100)

Folsom Prison Blues / Hey, Porter / So Doggone Lonesome / There You Go / Next in Line / Cry, Cry, Cry / I Walk the line / Don't Make Me Go / Train of Love / Home of the Blues / Get Rhythm

ORIGINAL GOLDEN HITS, VOL. 2
Sun Records (101)

Ballad of a Teen-age Queen / Come In, Stranger / The Ways of a Woman in Love / You're the Nearest Thing to Heaven / I Just Thought You'd Like To Know / Give My Love to Rose / Guess Things Happen That Way / Just About Time / Luther's Boogie / Thanks a Lot / Big River

STORY SONGS OF THE TRAINS AND RIVERS (JOHNNY CASH AND THE TENNESSEE TWO)
Sun Records (104)

Hey, Porter / Train of Love / Blue Train / I Heard That Lonesome Whistle / Port of Lonely Hearts / Wreck of the Old 97 / Rock Island Line / Big River / Wide Open Road / Down the Street to 301 / Life Goes On

GET RHYTHM
Sun Records (105)

Get Rhythm / Mean Eyed Cat / You Win Again / Country Boy / Two Timin' Woman / Oh Lonesome Me / Luther's Boogie / Doin' My Time / New Mexico / Belshazah / Sugartime

SHOWTIME
Sun Records (106)

Guess Things Happen That Way / Come In, Stranger / Rock Island Line / There You Go / Big River / Ballad of a Teenage Queen / I Walk the Line / The Wreck of the Old 97 / Cry, Cry, Cry / Hey, Porter / Folsom Prison Blues

JOHNNY CASH SINGS THE BALLADS OF THE TRUE WEST
Columbia Records C2S 838

Hiawatha's Vision / The Road to Kaintuck / The Shifting, Whispering Sands, Part I / The Ballad of Boot Hill / I Ride an Old Paint / Hardin Wouldn't Run / Mister Garfield / The Streets of Laredo / Johnny Reb / A Letter From Home / Bury Me Not on the Lone Prairie / Mean as Hell / Sam Hall / 25 Minutes To Go / The Blizzard / Sweet Betsy From Pike / Green Grow the Lilacs / Stampede / The Shifting, Whispering Sands, Part II / Reflections

THE FABULOUS JOHNNY CASH
Columbia Records CS 8122

Run Softly, Blue River / Frankie's Man, Johnny / That's All Over / The Troubadour / One More Ride / That's Enough / I Still Miss Someone / Don't Take Your Guns to Town / I'd Rather Die Young / Pickin' Time / Shepherd of My Heart / Supper-Time

SONGS OF OUR SOUL
Columbia Records CS 8148

Drink to Me / Five Feet High and Rising / The Man on the Hill / Hank and Joe and Me / Clementine / The Great Speckle Bird / I Want To Go Home / The Caretaker / Old Apache Squaw / Don't Step on Mother's Roses / My Grandfather's Clock / It Could Be You

RIDE THIS TRAIN
Columbia Records CS 8255

Loading Coal / Slow Rider / Lumberjack / Dorraine of Ponchartrain / Going to Memphis / When Papa Played the Dobro / Boss Jack / Old Doc Brown

THE SOUND OF JOHNNY CASH
Columbia Records CS 8602

Lost on the Desert / Accidentally on Purpose / In the Jailhouse Now / Mr. Lonesome / You Won't Have Far To Go / In Them Old Cottonfields Back Home / Delia's Gone / I Forgot More Than You'll Ever Know / You Remembered Me / I'm Free From the Chain Gang Now / Let Me Down Easy / Sing It Pretty, Sue

RING OF FIRE:
THE BEST OF JOHNNY CASH
Columbia Records CS 8853

Ring of Fire / I'd Still Be There / What Do I Care / I Still Miss Someone / Forty Shades of Green / Were You There /

The Rebel — Johnny Yuma / Bonanza / The Big Battle / Remember the Alamo / Tennessee Flat-Top Box / Peace in the Valley

I WALK THE LINE
Columbia Records CS 8990

I Walk the Line / Bad News / Folsom Prison Blues / Give My Love to Rose / Hey, Porter / I Still Miss Someone / Understand Your Man / Wreck of the Old 97 / Still in Town / Big River / Goodbye, Little Darlin', Goodbye / Troublesome Waters

BITTER TEARS
Columbia Records CS 9048

As Long as the Grass Shall Grow / Apache Tears / Custer / The Talking Leaves / The Ballad of Ira Hayes / Drums / White Girl / The Vanishing Race

FROM SEA TO SHINING SEA
Columbia Records CS 9447

From Sea to Shining Sea / The Whirl and the Suck / Call Daddy From the Mine / The Frozen Four-Hundred-Pound Fair-to-Middlin' Cotton Picker / The Walls of a Prison / The Masterpiece / You and Tennesee / Another Song To Sing / The Flint Arrowhead / Cisco Clifton's Fillin' Station / Shrimpin' Sailin' / From Sea to Shining Sea *(Finale)*

JOHNNY CASH'S GREATEST HITS, VOL. 1
Columbia Records CS 9478

Jackson *(with June Carter)* / I Walk the Line / Understand Your Man / Orange Blossom Special / The One on the Right Is on the Left / Ring of Fire / It Ain't Me, Babe / The Ballad of Ira Hayes / The Rebel — Johnny Yuma / Five Feet High and Rising / Don't Take Your Guns to Town

CARRYIN' ON WITH JOHNNY CASH AND JUNE CARTER
Columbia Records CS 9528

Long-Legged Guitar Pickin' Man / Shantytown / It Ain't Me, Babe / Fast Boat to Sydney / Pack Up Your Sorrows / I Got a Woman / Jackson / Oh, What a Good Thing We Had / You'll Be All Right / No, No, No / What'd I Say

JOHNNY CASH AT FOLSOM PRISON
Columbia Records CS 9639

Folsom Prison Blues / Dark as the Dungeon / I Still Miss Someone / Cocaine Blues / 25 Minutes To Go / Orange Blossom Special / The Long Black Veil / Send a Picture of Mother / The Wall / Dirty Old Egg-Sucking Dog / Flushed From the Bathroom of Your Heart / Jackson *(with June Carter)* / Give My Love to Rose *(with June Carter)* / I Got Stripes / Green, Green Grass of Home / Greystone Chapel

JOHNNY CASH IN THE HOLY LAND
Columbia Records KCS 9726

Prologue / Land of Israel / A Mother's Love / This Is Nazareth / Nazarene / Town of Cana / He Turned the Water Into Wine / My Wife June at the Sea of Galilee / Beautiful Words / Our Guide Jacob at Mount Tabor / The Ten Commandments / Daddy Sang Bass / At the Wailing Wall / Come to the Wailing Wall / In Bethlehem / In the Garden of Gethsemane / The Fourth Man / On the Via Dolorosa / Church of the Holy Sepulchre / At Calvary / God Is Not Dead

JOHNNY CASH AT SAN QUENTIN
Columbia Records CS 9827

Wanted Man / Wreck of the Old 97 / I Walk the Line / Darling Companion / Starkville City Jail / San Quentin / A Boy Named Sue / Peace in the Valley / Folsom Prison Blues

HELLO, I'M JOHNNY CASH
Columbia Records KCS 9943

If I Were a Carpenter / See Ruby Fall / Blistered / To Beat the Devil / I've Got a Thing About Trains / Route #1, Box 144 / Sing a Traveling Song / Wrinkled, Crinkled, Wadded Dollar Bill / 'Cause I Love You / The Devil to Pay / Southwind / Jesus Was a Carpenter

AWARDS 1956

BMI Award:

Folsom Prison Blues
I Walk the Line
So Doggone Lonesome

1957

The Cash Box Award:
The Most Programmed Male
Country Vocalist

BMI Award:

Next in Line
There You Go
Train of Love

1958

BMI Award:

Big River
Come In, Stranger
Home of the Blues
It's a Little More Like Heaven Where You Are

The Cash Box Award:
The Most Programmed Male
Country Vocalist

1959

BMI Award:

All Over Again
Don't Take Your Guns to Town
I Got Stripes
Luther Played the Boogie
What Do I Care?

1964

BMI Award:

The Matador
Understand Your Man

1967

GRAMMY Award:
Best Country and Western
Performance—duet, trio, or
group (vocal or instrumental)—
Jackson
—Johnny Cash,
June Carter (Columbia)

1968

GRAMMY Award:
Best Album Notes

(Annotator's Award)—

Johnny Cash at Folsom Prison

—Johnny Cash,
Annotator (Columbia)

GRAMMY Award:
Best Vocal Performance, male

Folsom Prison Blues,

Johnny Cash

Jackson

Johnny Cash and
June Carter

1969

Country Music Association
Annual Awards:
Entertainer of the Year
Single Album of the Year:

A Boy Named Sue

Album of the Year:

San Quentin

Male Vocalist of the Year
Vocal Group of the Year
(with June Carter)
Founding
President's Award—For
Outstanding Service to the

Country Music Association

The SESAC Award for

Lorena

Metronome Award—Man of
the Year
Gold Record Awards, awarded
by Record Industry Association
of America, Inc.

Ring of Fire

Johnny Cash,
Feb. 11, Columbia

I Walk the Line

Johnny Cash,
July 14, Columbia

BMI Award:

Folsom Prison Blues
Daddy Sang Bass

1970

GRAMMY Award:
Male Vocalist of the Year
Best Album Notes
(Annotator's Award)

Nashville Skyline

(Bob Dylan)—Johnny Cash,
Annotator (Columbia)

INDEX OF TITLES

Photograph Credits

Cash Family Album:
v, 6, 7, 8, 9, 10, 12,
14, 16, 18, 31, 36,
38

Joel Baldwin: xiv, 2,
20, 21, 22, 24, 26,
30, 32, 34, 35, 40,
42, 46, 47, 50, 51,
52, 53   Courtesy
Look Magazine

David Gahr: 4, 17

Courtesy, Columbia
Records: 15

Courtesy, ABC-TV:
19, 28, 48, 56

Joe Baker: 44, 62,
64, 65

Al Clayton: 55, 58,
60, 68, 228

Ira Friedlander:
66, 67

J. T. Phillips: 54, 61